MAN

Seyyed Hossein Nasr was born in Tehran where he received his early education. He later studied in the West and received his B.S. from the Massachusetts Institute of Technology and his M.A. and Ph.D. from Harvard University, where he studied the History of Science and Learning with special concentration on Islamic science and philosophy. In 1958 he returned to Iran and taught at Tehran University where he was Professor of the History of Science and Philosophy. From 1974 he was also president and founder of the Iranian Academy of Philosophy. He is now Professor of Islamic Studies at the George Washington University, Washington DC, in the USA. He is the author of *Ideals and Realities of Islam*, *Living Sufism* and *Islamic Life and Thought* (all Unwin Hyman).

OTHER WORKS BY SEYYED HOSSEIN NASR
IN EUROPEAN LANGUAGES

Three Muslim Sages
Ideals and Realities of Islam
An Introduction to Islamic Cosmological Doctrines
Science and Civilization in Islam
Living Sufism (also as Sufi Essays)
An Annotated Bibliography of Islamic Science
Islam and the Plight of Modern Man
Islamic Science: An Illustrated Study
The Transcendent Theosophy of Sadr al-Din Shirazi
Islamic Life and Thought
Knowledge and the Sacred
Islamic Art and Spirituality
Need for a Sacred Science
The Islamic Philosophy of Science

MAN AND NATURE

The Spiritual Crisis of
Modern Man

SEYYED HOSSEIN NASR

MANDALA
UNWIN PAPERBACKS
London   Boston   Sydney   Wellington

First published by George Allen & Unwin in 1968
Reprinted in 1976 and 1988

First published by Unwin® Paperbacks,
an imprint of Unwin Hyman Limited, in 1990

Unwin Hyman Limited
15–17 Broadwick Street, London W1V 1FP

Unwin Hyman, Inc.
8 Winchester Place, Winchester, Mass 01890, USA

Allen & Unwin Australia Pty Ltd
8 Napier Street, North Sydney, NSW 2060, Australia

Allen & Unwin New Zealand Pty Ltd in association with
the Port Nicholson Press, Compusales Building
75 Ghuznee Street, Wellington, New Zealand

British Library Cataloguing in Publication Data

Nasr, Seyyed Hossein, *1933–*
   [Encounter of man and nature] Man and nature.
1. Man. Ecology – Religious viewpoints
I. [Encounter of man and nature] II. Title
291.1'78362
ISBN 0-04-440620-7

Printed in Great Britain by Cox & Wyman Ltd, Reading

TO MARCO PALLIS

ACKNOWLEDGEMENTS

The lectures upon which this book are based, and part of the publication costs, were supported by a grant by the Rockefeller Foundaton to the University of Chicago.

PREFACE TO THE NEW EDITION

In the Name of God, Most Merciful,
Most Compassionate

It is a sign of the present state of humanity that only such blatant acts of aggression against nature as major oil spills, the burning of tropical forests and the consequences of man's rape of nature and his destructive technology in the form of the warming of the climate and the depleting of the ozone layer should turn the attention of modern man to the environmental crisis. It has taken the innocent eyes of dying seals to finally move hardened hearts and force human beings to think about the consequences of living on the earth as if no other creature mattered. When this book was first written, the ecological crisis had already arrived but few saw its consequences or spoke of it and fewer still sought to delve into the more profound causes for its occurrence. The rapidly deteriorating conditions of the environment soon made the crisis evident but still complacency continued until only recently when the external threat has become so great that a kind of popular reaction, a *vox populi*, has begun to make itself heard, joined by a chorus of experts who have finally joined the earlier lonely voices of environmentalists and nature lovers. Prophets of doom now abound and "green parties" have mushroomed everywhere.

The moving force for those movements remains, however, by and large purely external. For a humanity turned towards outwardness by the very processes of modernization, it is not so easy to see that the blight wrought upon the environment is in reality an externalization of the destitution of the inner state of the soul of that humanity whose actions are responsible for the ecological crisis. Consequently, overbearing summer heat, drought and dying seals have to remind us that all is not well in that earthly abode for whose sake modern man forewent his quest for Heaven and which he is now destroying with unprecedented ferocity.

And precisely because of the loss of the dimension of inwardness, much of the effort of those involved with environmental issues turns

3

to one form or another of environmental engineering. Many claim, for example, that if we could only change our means of transportation and diminish the use of fossil fuels as a source of energy, the problem would be solved or at least ameliorated. Few ask, however, why it is that modern man feels the need to travel so much. Why is the domicile of much of humanity so ugly and life so boring that the type of man most responsible for the environmental crisis has to escape the areas he has helped to vilify and take his pollution with him to the few still well-preserved areas of the earth in order to continue to function? Why must modern man consume so much and satiate his so-called needs only outwardly? Why is he unable to draw from any inward sustenance? We are, needless to say, not opposed to better care of the planet through the use of wiser means of production, transportation, etc. than those which exist today. Alternative forms of technology are to be welcomed and such institutions as the New Alchemy Institute of Cape Cod in America must be praised. But such feats of science and engineering alone will not solve the problem. There is no choice but to answer these and similar questions and to bring to the fore the spiritual dimension and the historical roots of the ecological crisis which many refuse to take into consideration to this day.

One of the chief causes for this lack of acceptance of the spiritual dimension of the ecological crisis is the survival of a scientism which continues to present modern science not as a particular way of knowing nature, but as a complete and totalitarian philosophy which reduces all reality to the physical domain and does not wish under any condition to accept the possibility of the existence of non-scientistic world-views. While not denying the legitimacy of a science limited to the physical dimension of reality, alternative world-views drawn from traditional doctrines remain constantly aware of the inner nexus which binds physical nature to the realm of the Spirit, and the outward face of things to an inner reality which they at once veil and reveal. This reductionism and scientism has prevented Western science, for the most part, from turning to the more inward causes of the environmental crisis, while many individual scientists become ever more interested in ecological questions and even somewhat more responsible for the often catastrophic effects of their "disinterested" and "pure" research.

Preface to the New Edition

During the past two decades as awareness of the environmental crisis has increased, numerous vocal groups and even political parties have sprung up to defend the environment. Until recently, however, most of these have had a leftish tendency with a tone decisively opposed to established religions, although this is now changing somewhat. While some have sought to convert the ecological movement into a religion itself, many who are also interested in religion have turned to religious movements of doubtful origin and in any case outside the established churches in the West. The churches, meanwhile, did not react until quite recently to develop "a theology of ecology" drawing from the depth of the Christian tradition as suggested originally in this book. At the same time, a few marginal figures who have taken the ecological crisis seriously from a Christian theological point of view have either moved away from theological orthodoxy or been disowned by the mainstream established churches. Still, there is some sign of hope in this direction as the spiritual legacy of certain branches of the orthodox Christian tradition, such as the Celtic Church with its love of nature, begins to be resuscitated in certain quarters.

In the meantime, much of the onus of responsibility for the ecological crisis is placed by many scientists, historians and even a few theologians, not upon certain developments within Western civilization starting with the late Middle Ages, the Renaissance and the seventeenth century, but upon the whole of the monotheistic tradition as seen in the writings of as well known a figure as Arnold Toynbee. Such thinkers forget that the pure monotheism of Islam which belongs to the same Abrahamic tradition as Judaism and Christianity never lost sight of the sacred quality of nature as asserted by the Quran, and that Oriental Christianity and Judaism never developed the attitude of simple domination and plunder of nature that developed later in the history of the West.

The result of this frontal attack against the monotheistic religions in general and Western Christianity in particular by many proponents of a sane ecological policy, combined until recently with an aloofness on the part of orthodox Christian theologians towards the theological significance of nature and the need for its "resacralization", has led to a

5

strange wedding in many instances between ecological movements and all kinds of pseudo-religious sects or the development of such heterodox and in fact dangerous so-called "synthese" as "the new religion" of Teilhardism. In either case despite claims to the contrary, the ecological movement has become deprived of the revivifying breath of authentic spirituality and the significance of the veritable spiritual dimension of the ecological crisis has become forgotten, for there is no authentic spirituality without orthodoxy understood in the most universal sense of the term.

Modern man, faced with the unprecedented crisis of his own making which now threatens the life of the whole planet, still refuses to see where the real causes of the problem lie. He turns his gaze to the Book of Genesis and the rest of the Bible as the source of the crisis rather than looking upon the gradual de-sacralization of the cosmos which took place in the West and especially the rationalism and humanism of the Renaissance which made possible the Scientific Revolution and the creation of a science whose function, according to Francis Bacon, one of its leading proponents, was to gain power over nature, dominate her and force her to reveal her secrets not for the glory of God but for the sake of gaining worldly power and wealth.

Today, this forest is destroyed because of man's rights; that sea is polluted because of man's supposed needs. Man is made absolute, his "rights" dominating over both God's rights and the rights of His creation. Medieval European man was always aware that only God was absolute and that he was relative. Even if he did not often heed the call of certain of his saints and sages such as St Francis, to appreciate the salvific beauty of the natural order, he never dreamt of turning himself and especially his earthly existence into something absolute. The very reality of the Beyond prevented him from sacrificing everything for an earthly life which would in any case be transitory, and the very blinding Majesty of God as the Absolute made it impossible for him ever to consider himself as being in any way absolute. The absolutization of the human state is a heritage of the European Renaissance whose deadly consequences are being manifested only today, even if few realize even now the dangerous role of this humanism in the present impasse created in man's relation with the natural order.

6

This humanism, embedded strangely enough in the anti-humanism of scientific rationalism, refuses to see the underlying causes of the ecological crisis and cuts Western man from the very spiritual sources which could help save him from the present crisis. Nothing is more dangerous in the current ecological debate than that scientistic view of man and nature which cuts man from his spiritual roots and takes a desacralized nature for granted while expanding its physical boundaries by billions of light years. This view destroys the reality of the spiritual world while speaking of awe before the grandeur of the cosmos. It destroys man's centrality in the cosmic order and his access to the spiritual world while speaking of the incredible science-fiction of the evolution of man from the original soup of molecules which supposedly contained the whole of cosmic reality at the beginning following the big bang. Having devastated nature through the application of a science of a purely material order combined with greed, modern man now wishes to put the blame at the door of the whole Western religious tradition. But because the reality of the Spirit is such that it cannot be denied by any form of sophism or limited science of the material order, the ecological crisis cannot be solved without paying particular attention to the spiritual dimension of the problem. Nor can one ignore the historical roots of this crisis which reveal the significance of the spiritual and intellectual factors involved and make evident the role of religion in the unfolding of the drama which has led to the present crisis.

In the pages which follow we have sought to delve into the roots of the ecological crisis through recourse to the history of science as well as philosophy and religion in the West. Since the rise of awareness in the ecological crisis, some effort has been spent to make correct use of these disciplines and especially the history of science to clarify the roots of the present day impasse, but these efforts have been minor compared to the dimensions of the problems. Most historians of science still see the subject of their field as the continuous glorious march of science towards an even greater degree of knowledge of and power over nature. The positivism of the history of science which has dominated the field since its founding by E. Mach and G. Sarton, whose perspective gained victory over the non-positivistic views of

P. Duhem, continues to hold sway over most practitioners of the discipline. Nor is the situation much better in the field of philosophy with the dominating positivism which pervades it.

As far as the history of science is concerned, during the 1960s and the student unrest in American universities at least one group of students invaded a history of science department in a leading American university specifically demanding a new role for the history of science, which should not be to trace the major "breakthroughs" of science but to explain how the cultivation and application of Western science has placed man in such a desperate position. Yet, by and large, a transformation of aim and direction on the part of this discipline in the West is not observable anywhere on a major scale, and the interest of students in studying the history of science to discover other sciences of nature and means of finding a path out of the present day morass usually outruns the interest of professors teaching them. This is still the norm despite a few notable exceptions.

We had also originally proposed the rediscovery of the traditional cosmologies of the Oriental traditions as means of gaining a new vision of the world of nature and its significance. This too has taken place to a notable degree in the years that have passed, but not always in a meaningful or wholesome way. There have been fine new translations and expositions of authentic traditional sources bearing upon the symbolism of natural forms and various traditional cosmologies. But for the most part the flood of material on these subjects has entered the arena of modern man's life garbed in the dress of occultism and riding the wave of the pseudo-religious movements with which so much of this type of material is associated. It seems that again with certain noteworthy exceptions (seen in the writings of such men as Huston Smith, Theodore Roszak, Wolfgang Smith and Jacob Needleman in America and Keith Critchlow, Gilbert Durand and Elemire Zolla in Europe—men who have sought to rediscover the traditional sciences from the traditional perspective), there is now an extreme polarization of a most dangerous kind. Departments of philosophy and much of the humanities in universities continue to be immersed in the closed world of logic devoid of transcendence, while the "fringe" or "counter-culture" is seeking for transcendence (often in the dress of immanence) but is impervious to the logic which emanates from the inner Intellect and also to revelation, which is also a manifestation of the Universal Intellect or Logos. How rare is that vision contained in the majestic work of Frithjof Schuon, *Logic and Transcendence*, where from the perspective of tradition a universal panorama is unfolded in which both logic and transcendence receive their appropriate due.

Finally, in the pages which follow we had clearly stated that the ecological crisis is only an externalization of an inner malaise and cannot be solved without a spiritual rebirth of Western man. This theme has been followed forcefully by a number of authors since this work was first written including Theodore Roszak in his *Where the Wasteland Ends* and occasionally in certain of his other writings and Philip Sherrard in his *The Rape of Man and Nature*. However, except for the exponents of traditional doctrines such as Frithjof Schuon, Titus Burckhardt, Marco Pallis and Martin Lings, whose works are often cited in this book, the forces for a genuine renewal within the religious traditions in the West have not advanced appreciably, there being notable exceptions such as those who follow the teachings of Thomas Merton. There have also been noteworthy groups interested in the Western tradition but not of a directly religious background such as the Lindisfarne School and the *Temenos* circle which are worth mentioning in this connection. Nevertheless, it has been the forces that wish to repeat the errors of modernism within the very structure of Western religious doctrines and rites that have gained ascendancy, forcing many thoughtful people to seek elsewhere for genuine traditional teachings.

It is still our hope that as the crisis created by man's forgetfulness of who he really is grows and that as the idols of his own making crumble one by one before his eyes, he will begin a true reform of himself, which always means a spiritual rebirth and through his rebirth attain a new harmony with the world of nature around him. Otherwise, it is hopeless to expect to live in harmony with that grand theophany which is virgin nature, while remaining oblivious and indifferent to the Source of that theophany both beyond nature and at the centre of man's being. May the following pages be a humble aid in drawing attention to the roots of the problems of which so many discern the outward signs, roots which lie deep in the hardened and forgetful mind of modern man, whose destiny nevertheless calls upon him to fulfil his role as God's viceregent on earth, protector of the natural order, and witness to the truth that *Omnis natura Deo loquitur* (The whole of nature speaks of God).[1] To destroy the natural environment is therefore to fail in one's humanity. It is to commit a veritable crime against creation, for "The seven heavens and the earth and all that they contain extol His limitless Glory; and there is not a single thing but extols His limitless Glory and Praise."[2]

SEYYED HOSSEIN NASR
Washington, DC
October 1989 AD
Rabi' al-awwal 1410 AH

[1]   Hugo of St Victor, *Eruditio Didascalica*, 6.5 p. 176, 1.805.
[2]   Quran XVI (Banu Isra'il); 44, Muhammad Asad trans. modified.

CONTENTS

INTRODUCTION

The chapters of this book are based on four lectures delivered at the University of Chicago during May 1966, and forming part of a series of annual lectures that take place at that University under the sponsorship of the Rockefeller Foundation. The aim of these lectures is to investigate in the broadest sense the problems posed for peace and human life itself by the various applications of modern science.

The very fact that such lectures are held annually attests the apprehension existing in many circles today about the misdeeds of technology and the threat of science and technology to peace. Causes are sought for the present disorder whose existence is so obvious that few can any longer afford to ignore it. But only rarely have the underlying and essential causes been brought to light perhaps partly because if they were to be made known there would have to be a radical change in the very thought pattern of many of those who discern the ill effects of these causes. And this change few are willing to accept or to undergo.

Everyone talks today of the danger of war, over-population or the pollution of air and water. But usually the same people who discern these obvious problems speak of the necessity of further 'development', or war against 'human misery' stemming from conditions imposed by terrestrial existence itself. In other words they wish to remove the problems brought about by the destruction of the equilibrium between man and nature through further conquest and domination of nature. Few would be willing to admit that the acutest social and technical problems facing mankind today come not from so-called 'under development' but from 'over-development'. Few are willing to look reality in the face and accept the fact that there is no peace possible in human society as long as the attitude toward nature and the whole natural environment is one based on aggression and war. Furthermore, perhaps not all realize that in order to gain this peace with nature there must be peace with the spiritual order. To be at peace with the Earth one must be at peace with Heaven.

There is no way for man to defend his humanity and not be dragged through his own inventions and machinations to the infra-human, except by remaining faithful to the image of man as a reflection of something that transcends the merely human. Peace in human society and the preservation of human values are impossible without peace with the natural and spiritual orders and respect for the immutable supra-human realities which are the source of all that is called 'human values'.

The thesis presented in this book is simply this: that although science is legitimate in itself, the role and function of science and its application have become illegitimate and even dangerous because of the lack of a higher form of knowledge into which science could be integrated and the destruction of the sacred and spiritual value of nature. To remedy this situation the metaphysical knowledge pertaining to nature must be revived and the sacred quality of nature given back to it once again. In order to accomplish this end the history and philosophy of science must be reinvestigated in relation to Christian theology and the traditional philosophy of nature which existed during most of European history. Christian doctrine itself should be enlarged to include a doctrine concerning the spiritual significance of nature and this with the aid of Oriental metaphysical and religious traditions where such doctrines are still alive. These traditions would not be so much a source of new knowledge as an aid to *anamnesis*, to the remembrance of teachings within Christianity now mostly forgotten. The result would be the bestowal once again of a sacred quality upon nature, providing a new background for the sciences without negating their value or legitimacy within their own domain. It would be the very antithesis of the movement current today under the name of 'secular theology'. It would mean not to secularize theology but to bestow a theological and sacred significance upon what modern man considers to be most secular of all domains, namely science.

When we were invited to deliver these lectures in 1966, the

choice of our name was due particularly to the fact of our being a follower of a non-Western religion and culture, yet somewhat acquainted with modern science and its history and philosophy. In accepting this perhaps audacious task of acting as an Oriental critic of the West and thus reversing what orientalists have been doing for over a century about all Eastern cultures and religions, we felt it was imperative to step beyond the boundaries of modern science or even the disciplines of the history and philosophy of science to delve into questions of a metaphysical and theological order. Furthermore, in carrying out the programme outlined above we also had to step beyond the confines of Western civilization into the vast domain that is called comparative religion today. This whole travail was undertaken with the hope of finding once again a sacred foundation for science itself.

To carry out such a vast programme requires knowledge of many disciplines and access to sources in many languages. We do not by any means claim to possess a mastery of all of these domains nor of all the languages involved. Because of these reasons as well as the limited time at our disposal for the preparation of these lectures, we have often made use of secondary sources. In fact most of the notes, excluding those which serve as reference, are meant to be additional support for our arguments and not their scholarly proof. The thesis presented is essentially metaphysical and philosophical and should be considered in itself irrespective of whether all the necessary scholarly footnotes are provided or not. In the notes we have not sought to exhaust the sources that substantiate our position nor to provide all the scholarly proofs necessary to convince the sceptical reader but to provide certain evidence and to point out the way for further investigation by others. These essays do not claim at all to be exhaustive but are a humble introduction to a type of investigation that has not as yet been pursued to any appreciable extent. To do full justice to all the themes treated here would need many volumes and the collaboration of many scholars working in a domain that cuts across several academic disciplines including the history of science, philosophy of science and comparative religion. We only hope that the ideas presented here will stimulate some thinking in a constructive direction toward the solution of a problem that is both urgent and vital and will not simply be brushed aside by the would-be critics because of lack of full historical and scholarly evidence, a role which these essays have not been meant to fulfil.

In conclusion we wish to thank the Divinity School, the Department of Biological Sciences and the Center of Middle Eastern Studies of the University of Chicago who acted as host for these lectures and to Dean Jerald Brauer and particularly Professor John Rust of the same University for their assistance and kindness in making both the lectures and their publication possible.

SEYYED HOSSEIN NASR

Tehran
December 1967
Ramadan 1387

Chapter 1

The Problem

Of late, numerous studies have been made concerning the crisis brought about by modern science and its applications, but few have sought the profound intellectual and historical causes that are responsible for this state of affairs. When invited to deliver a series of lectures in this University on the meaning of war and struggle for the preservation of human dignity under conditions which threaten human existence itself, we felt that it would be more appropriate to deal with principles and causes rather than contingencies and effects, one of which is the problem of moral action on the social and human level, together with the possible consequence of war which modern technology and science have made total. We hope, therefore, to state the problem which has resulted from the encounter of man and nature today, then to seek the underlying causes that have brought this condition about and to cite the principles whose neglect have made the modern crisis so acute.

Today, almost everyone living in the urbanized centres of the Western world feels intuitively a lack of something in life. This is due directly to the creation of an artificial environment from which nature has been excluded to the greatest possible extent. Even the religious man in such circumstances has lost the sense of the spiritual significance of nature.[1] The domain of nature has become a 'thing' devoid of meaning, and at the same time the void created by the disappearance of this vital aspect of human existence continues to live within the souls of men and to manifest itself in many ways, sometimes violently and desperately. Furthermore, even this type of secularized and urbanized existence is itself threatened, through the very domination of nature that has made it possible, so that the crisis brought about through the encounter of man and nature and the application of the modern sciences of nature to technology has become a matter of common concern.[2]

Despite all the official clamour about the ever increasing domination over nature, and the so-called progress which is supposed to be its economic concomitant, many realize in their hearts that the castles they are building are on sand and that there is a disequilibrium between man and nature that threatens all man's apparent victory over nature.

The dangers brought about by man's domination over nature are too well known to need elucidation. Nature has become desacralized for modern man, although this process itself has been carried to its logical conclusion only in the case of a small minority.[3] Moreover, nature has come to be regarded as something to be used and enjoyed to the fullest extent possible. Rather than being like a married woman from whom a man benefits but also towards whom he is responsible, for modern man nature has become like a prostitute—to be benefited from without any sense of obligation and responsibility toward her. The difficulty is that the condition of prostituted nature is becoming such as to make any further enjoyment of it impossible. And, in fact, that is why many have begun to worry about its condition.

It is precisely the 'domination of nature' that has caused the problem of over-population, the lack of 'breathing space', the coagulation and congestion of city life, the exhaustion of natural resources of all kinds, the destruction of natural beauty, the marring of the living environment by means of the machine and its products, the abnormal rise in mental illnesses and a thousand and one other difficulties some of which appear completely insurmountable.[4] And finally, it is the same 'domination of nature', limited to external nature and coupled with giving complete freedom to the animal nature within man, that has made the problem of war so crucial, war which seems unavoidable, yet because of its total and almost 'cosmic' nature brought about by modern technology, must be avoided.

The sense of domination over nature and a materialistic conception of nature on the part of modern man are combined, moreover, with a lust and sense of greed which makes an ever greater demand upon the environment.[5] Incited by the elusive dream of economic progress, considered as an end in itself, a sense of the unlimited power of man and his possibilities is developed, together with the belief, particularly well developed in America, of boundless and illimitable possibilities within things, as if the world of forms were not finite and bound by the very limits of those forms.[6]

Man wants to dominate nature not only for economic motives but also for a 'mystique' which is a direct residue of a one-time spiritual relation *vis-à-vis* nature. Men no longer climb spiritual mountains—or at least rarely do so. They now want to conquer all mountain peaks.[7] They wish to deprive the mountain of all its majesty by overcoming it—preferably through the most difficult line of ascent. When the experience of flight to the heavens, symbolized in Christianity by the spiritual experience of the *Divine Comedy* and in Islam by the nocturnal ascension (*al-mi'râj*) of the Prophet Muḥammad (upon whom be peace) is no longer available to men, there remains the urge to fly into space and conquer the heavens. There is everywhere the desire to conquer nature, but in the process the value of the conqueror himself, who is man, is destroyed and his very existence threatened.

Rather than man deciding the value of science and technology, these creations of man have become the criteria of man's worth and value.[8] Practically the only protest that is heard is that of the conservationists and other lovers of nature. Their voice, although of much value, is not fully heard because their arguments are often taken as being sentimental rather than intellectual. Well-known theologians and philosophers have for the most part remained silent or have bent backwards in order to avoid offending the prevailing scientific mood of the day. Only rarely has any voice been raised to show that the current belief in the domination of nature is the usurpation, from the religious point of view, of man's role as the custodian and guardian of nature.[9]

The sciences of nature themselves, which are in one sense the fruit, and in another the cause of the present crisis of man's encounter with nature, have themselves, through a gradual process which we shall examine later, become secularized. And this secularized knowledge of nature divorced from the vision of God in nature has become accepted as the sole legitimate form of science.[10] Moreover, due to the distance separating the scientist from the layman a major distortion and discrepancy has been created between scientific theories and their vulgarization upon which their supposed theological and philosophical implications are too often based.[11]

Altogether one can say that the problem concerns both the sciences and the means whereby they are understood, interpreted and applied. There are crises in the domains of both understanding and application. The power of reason given to man, his *ratio*, which is like the projection or subjective prolongation of the intellect or the *intellectus*, divorced from its principle, has become like an acid that burns its way through the fibre of cosmic order and threatens to destroy itself in the process. There is nearly total disequilibrium between modern man and nature as attested by nearly every expression of modern civilization which seeks to offer a challenge to nature rather than to co-operate with it.

That the harmony between man and nature has been destroyed, is a fact which most people admit. But not everyone realizes that this disequilibrium is due to the destruction of the harmony between man and God.[12] It involves a relationship which concerns all knowledge. And in fact the modern sciences themselves are the fruit of a set of factors which, far from being limited to the domain of nature, concern all Western man's intellectual and religious heritage. Because of this, or often as a reaction against it, the modern sciences have come into being. That is the reason why it is necessary to begin our analysis by turning firstly to the natural sciences and the views held concerning their philosophical and theological significance, and then to the limitations inherent within them which are responsible for the crisis that their application, and the acceptance of their world view, have brought about for modern man.

It must never be forgotten that for non-modern man—whether he be ancient or contemporary—the very stuff of the Universe has a sacred aspect. The cosmos speaks to man and all of its phenomena contain meaning. They are symbols of a higher degree of reality which the cosmic domain at once veils and reveals. The very structure of the cosmos contains a spiritual message for man and is thereby a revelation coming from the same source as religion itself.[13] Both are the manifestations of the Universal Intellect, the Logos, and the cosmos itself is an integral part of that total Universe of meaning in which man lives and dies.[14]

In order for the modern sciences of nature to come into being, the substance of the cosmos had first to be emptied of its sacred character and become profane. The world view of modern science, especially as propagated through its vulgarization, itself contributed to this secularization of nature and of natural substances. The symbols in nature became facts, entities in themselves that are totally divorced from other orders of reality. The cosmos which had been transparent thus became opaque and spiritually meaningless—at least to those who were totally immersed in the scientific view of nature—even if individual scientists believed otherwise. The traditional sciences such as alchemy, which can be compared to the celebration of a cosmic mass, became reduced to a chemistry in which the substances had lost all their sacramental character. In the process, the sciences of nature lost their symbolic intelligibility, a fact that is most directly responsible for the crisis which the modern scientific world view and its applications have brought about.[15]

The quantitative character of modern science must be pointed out in particular because it exists as a general tendency which seeks as an ideal the reduction of all quality to quantity and all that is essential in the metaphysical sense to the material and substantial.[16] The suffocating material environment created by industrialization and mechanization, which is felt by all who live in large urban centres of today, is a consequence of the purely material and quantitative nature of the sciences whose applications have made industrialization possible. Moreover, due to the lack of a total world view of a metaphysical nature into which the modern sciences could be integrated, the symbolic aspect of number and quantity is itself forgotten. The Pythagorean-Platonic number theory has been made to appear, like so many other traditional sciences, as an old wives' tale.

The quantitative sciences of nature which, moreover, are a possible and in the appropriate circumstances legitimate science, come in fact to be the only valid and acceptable sciences of nature. All other knowledge of the natural and cosmic orders is deprived of the status of science and relegated to the rank of sentimentality or superstition. It seems as if modern science has made a condition of its acceptance the rejection of knowledge about the root of existence itself, although again many scientists as individuals may not share this view.[17] The total impact of modern science on the mentality of men has been to provide them with a knowledge of the accidents of things, provided they are willing to forgo a knowledge of the substance that underlies all things. And it is this limitation which threatens the most dire circumstances for man as an integral being.[18]

The very restrictive outlook connected with modern science makes the knowledge of cosmology in the true sense impossible in the matrix of the modern scientific world view. Cosmology is a science dealing with all orders of formal reality, of which the material order is but one aspect. It is a sacred science which is bound to be connected to revelation and metaphysical doctrine in whose bosom alone it becomes meaningful and efficacious. Today there is no modern cosmology, and the use of the word is really a usurpation of a term whose original meaning has been forgotten.[19] A cosmology which is based solely on the material and corporeal level of existence, however far it may extend into the galaxies, and which is moreover based on individual conjectures that change from day to day, is not real cosmology. It is a generalized view of a terrestrial physics and chemistry, and as

a vital concept

has been pointed out by certain Christian theologians and philosophers, it is really devoid of any direct theological significance unless it be by accident.[20] Moreover, it is based on a material physics which tends to ever greater analysis and division of matter with the ideal of reaching the 'ultimate' matter at the basis of the world, an ideal however, which can never be attained because of the ambiguity and unintelligibility lying within the nature of matter and the border of chaos separating formal matter from that 'pure matter' which medieval philosophers called *materia prima*.[21]

The disappearance of a real cosmology in the West is due in general to the neglect of metaphysics, and more particularly to a failure to remember the hierarchies of being and of knowledge. The multiple levels of reality are reduced to a single psychophysical domain, as if the third dimension were suddenly to be taken out of our vision of a landscape. As a result, not only has cosmology become reduced to the particular sciences of material substances, but in a more general sense the tendency of reducing the higher to the lower, and conversely trying to make the greater come into being out of the lesser, has become widely prevalent. With the destruction of all notion of hierarchy in reality, the rapport between degrees of knowledge and the correspondence between various levels of reality upon which the ancient and medieval sciences were based have disappeared, causing these sciences to appear as superstition (in the etymological sense of this word) and as something whose principle or basis has been destroyed or forgotten.

Metaphysics is similarly reduced to rationalistic philosophy, and this philosophy itself has become gradually the ancillary of the natural and mathematical sciences, to the extent that some modern schools consider the only role of philosophy to be to elucidate the methods and clarify the logical consistencies of the sciences. The independent critical function which reason should exercise *vis-à-vis* science, which is its own creation, has disappeared so that this child of the human mind has itself become the judge of human values and the criterion of truth. In this process of reduction in which the independent and critical role of philosophy has itself been surrendered to the edicts of modern science, it is often forgotten that the scientific revolution of the seventeenth century is itself based upon a particular philosophical position. It is not *the* science of nature but *a* science making certain assumptions as to the nature of reality, time, space, matter, etc.[22] But once these assumptions were made and a science came into being based upon them, they have been comfortably forgotten and the results of this science made to be the determining factor as to the true nature of reality.[23] That is why it is necessary to turn, albeit briefly, to the view of modern scientists and philosophers of science as to the significance of modern science especially physics in determining the meaning of the total nature of things. Whether we like it or not, it is precisely such views that determine much of the modern conception of nature accepted by the general public, and they are thereby important elements in the general problem of the encounter of man and nature.

Without going into detail regarding the different schools of the philosophy of science, a task for which others are much better prepared than we, and which has in fact been carried out fully in several recent works,[24] it is necessary to describe some of the trends which pertain more directly to our discussion. Of these perhaps the most influential, certainly in English speaking countries, has been logical positivism born from the Vienna circle of R. Carnap, Ph. Frank, H. Reichenbach and others.[25] Seeking to remove the last spectre of metaphysical significance from modern science, the followers of this school believe that it is not for science to discover the nature of things, or some aspect of the real. It is to establish connections between mathematical and physical signs (which they call symbols) that can be elaborated through the external senses and scientific instruments, concerning that experience which appears to us as the external world.

Although this school has been instrumental in codifying and clarifying some of the definitions and logical procedures of modern science, particularly physics, it has also deprived science

24

of the most important element that the Middle Ages bequeathed to it, namely the quest for the real. Contrary to the Greek astronomers and mathematicians, for whom the role of mathematical sciences was to conceive of conceptual models which 'save the phenomena', the Muslim scientists, followed later by the Latins, believed that even in the domain of the mathematical sciences the function of science was to discover an aspect of the real. They applied the realism of Aristotelian biology and physics to the domain of the most exact mathematical science of the day, namely astronomy, and converted the epicyclic system of Ptolemy from mathematical configurations to crystalline spheres which formed a part of the real texture of the Universe.

In a later work of Ptolemy, of course, allusion is made to the crystalline nature of the heavens. Yet it was the Muslim mathematicians, followed by the Latin scientists, who universalized this indication and made it a principle of all science to seek knowledge of that domain of reality with which it is concerned. This attitude was so central that despite the revolt of seventeenth century science, especially against Aristotelianism, the belief that science seeks to discover the nature of physical reality survived from Galileo and Newton to modern times. It must also be added that the positivists, who claim they are returning to the point of view of the Greek mathematicians and astronomers against the realism of the Peripatetics, forget the fact that the Greek mathematicians were also seeking after a knowledge of the real. For them, however, reality was not in phenomena but in mathematical relations, which themselves possessed an ontological status thanks to the Pythagorean philosophy, by which their thought was permeated.

The positivistic interpretation of science is, in reality, an aim to de-ontologize science completely—not by shifting the ontological status from the physical domain to the Pythagorean-Platonic world of archetypes connected with mathematics, but by denying its ontological significance completely. It is with justice that a critic of the positivist school such as J. Maritain accuses it of confusing an empiriological analysis of things with their ontological analysis, and adds that modern physics 'de-ontologizes things'.[26] Likewise, certain philosophers of science, chief among them E. Meyerson, have insisted on the ontological aspect that all science must perforce possess.[27]

Closely akin to the positivist attitude is that of the operationalists connected in the domain of physics mostly with the name of P. Bridgman. Based on the background of a disdain for a unified world view and a monolithic methodology for science, this school ties all significance in science to operations which can define its concepts. The operation itself, rather than the real, is the ultimate matrix of scientific knowledge. There is in the operational philosophy a tinge of the pluralistic world of William James, namely a disdain for a total philosophical and methodological background for science characteristic of the Anglo-Saxon mentality in general, as compared with that of the Continent. One is reminded of the famous saying that 'science is what scientists do'. There are different domains of inquiry lacking a unified and universal theory;[28] 'a multiverse rather than a Universe' to quote the phrase of R. Oppenheimer.

Another school, which again bears a relationship to the positivist point of view in its denial of a connection between the concepts of science and the real, is sometimes called logical non-realist. Among its members, the most outstanding are H. Poincaré and P. Duhem, both well-known mathematicians and physicists. Duhem is also an eminent historian of science,[29] and so in a sense is E. Mach, both physicist and philosopher and historian of science. The question of whether other forms of knowledge can reach the ground of reality is not relevant here, for the different members of this school have held different views on the matter. The ground on which they do agree is that the concepts derived by intellection, and which constitute the laws and unimpeachable content of modern science, are not discovered aspects of reality with an ontological aspect. Rather, they are irreducible mental concepts and subjective conventions of a linguistic nature established by scientists so that they in turn can establish communication with each other. Science is thereby conceived of as knowledge of subjective notions rather than of the existence of an objective reality.[30]

There are others, like E. Cassirer followed by H. Morgenau, who accept the irreducible concepts of science, and employ them, but only as regulative concepts. For them these concepts are accepted 'as if' they existed but actually possess only a regulative status.[31] This group, which has been called neo-Kantian precisely because of its acceptance of the *als ob* status of concepts, a point of view which after Kant was to be systematized by Vaihinger, must therefore also be considered as non-realist and opposed to granting science the power to understand the nature of things.

There is further the group of logical realists opposed to the two above for whom concepts derived through the intellect have a logically realistic status; they refer to an ontological object of knowledge. Among this group may be mentioned A. Grünebaum and F. S. C. Northrop, both of whom emphasize the correspondence between the concepts of mathematical physics and the real.[32] Northrop especially seeks to show that both the New-tonian-Kantian world of mathematical physics and the qualitative vision of nature emphasized by Goethe, which he calls natural historical, and whose knowledge is immediate and aesthetic rather than abstract and mathematical, are ultimately real.[33] The world is order or cosmos rather than chaos, one that is alive as an organism and at the same time governed by law.[34] But once again in this school it is emphasized that the knowledge derived from the sciences is the way that leads us to an ultimate knowledge of things. There is no hierarchy of knowledge, only a knowledge of the corporeal domain which determines knowledge as such.

Among scientists themselves, particularly physicists, there have been many who have realized that by being bound to quantitative relationships science can never gain a knowledge of the ultimate nature and root of things, but is bound to move always within the closed and subjective world of 'pointer readings' and mathematical concepts. This view made popular particularly by A.

Eddington[35] and in another vein by J. Jeans has been used to a great extent by non-scientists to show the limitations of science or the 'ideal' character of the world. Again, however, it has not served the purpose of defining the domain of scientific knowledge within a universal hierarchy of knowledge. Nevertheless the thesis of Eddington that science because of its method is selective and bound to a 'subjectively-selected knowledge' is certainly of significance; yet it deals with only an aspect of reality and not the whole of it, in the question of the relation between science, philosophy and religion. It is a point of view that has been also expounded, although in quite a different fashion, by A. N. Whitehead. His process philosophy of nature has also sought to display the richness of a reality with which science deals only in part.[36]

Other scientists have insisted that, rather than being a unified methodological pursuit of knowledge, science is so inextricably tied to the practice and history of science that its premisses cannot be independently formulated.[37] It is a total activity, and there is no point in speaking of a distinct and explicit philosophy and method of science. Likewise, some scientists insist that physics or other sciences cannot prove or disprove any particular philosophic thesis, whether it be materialistic or idealistic, and that one should not seek philosophical implications of scientific theories and views.[38] Needless to say, this perspective is not totally accepted, especially by non-scientist vulgarizers of science who often see more general implications in scientific theories than the scientists themselves.

In contrast to this group, certain other scientists have seen the deepest implications in the theories of modern science whether it be relativity or quantum mechanics, the corpuscular theories of light or the principle of indeterminacy.[39] Only too often the significance of a particular scientific discovery is lifted far above the confines of the domain of physics itself, as if the self-imposed restrictions of modern science, which by its choosing is limited to the quantitative aspect of things, were non-existent. The theory of relativity is made to imply that there is nothing absolute, as if all reality were only physical motion. The principle of indeterminacy is made to mean the freedom of the human will or lack of a nexus of causality between things. The hypothesis of evolution, itself a child of nineteenth-century philosophy, becomes a dogma of biology presented to the world as an axiomatic truth and furthermore a mental fashion that pervades all realms so that one no longer studies anything in itself but only its evolution or history.

In this question the non-scientists have in fact proceeded much further than the scientists themselves, especially in biology and the question of evolution. Sometimes the most shallow proofs are presented for a particular religious or philosophical truth as if the only acceptable proof were recently discovered scientific theories. How often has one heard in classrooms and from pulpits that physics through the principle of indeterminacy 'allows' man to be free, as if the lesser could ever determine the greater, or as if human freedom could be determined externally by a science which is contained in human consciousness itself.

It must be added that many physicists are seriously concerned with philosophical and religious problems, often more than those who deal with the social and psychological sciences. Moreover, some physicists, in trying to find solutions to dilemmas placed before them by modern physics, have turned to Oriental doctrines —usually with genuine interest but rarely with the necessary intellectual attitude to grasp their full import. Among those most seriously interested in this field one may mention R. Oppenheimer and E. Schrödinger. The latter, who has written much on the philosophy of modern physics, in his particular concern with the problem of the multiplicity of consciousnesses who share the world, has turned to Hindu doctrines for a solution. To explain this multiplicity he believes that one of two miracles must be true, either the existence of a real external world, or the admission that all things and all consciousnesses are aspects of a single reality, the One.[40] The world is *maya* which does not concern 'me', the consciousness which says 'I'. Oriental metaphysics would at this point add that it is not a matter of choosing between the two miracles. Both are true but each on its own level. The miracle of existence itself is the greatest of all miracles for those who reside in the domain of existing things, while from the point of view of the One, the Absolute, there is no 'otherness' or 'separation'. All things are one, not materially and substantially but inwardly and essentially. Again it is a question of realizing the levels of reality and the hierarchy of the different domains of being.

Nor have the scientists been totally negligent of the theological and religious problems which the vulgarization of the scientific view and a neglect of its inherent limitations have brought about. A few, like C. F. von Weizäcker, have even been concerned about the scepticism caused by modern science and have tried to deal in a meaningful way with the encounters of theology and modern science.[41] In this domain these writings are sometimes more serious and pertinent than some of the works of professional theologians. This latter group has singularly neglected the question of nature, and when it has considered it has been often led to irrelevant or secondary problems. Religious authors have, moreover, often exhibited a sense of inferiority and fear before modern science which has led to an ever greater submission to and adoptation of scientific views with the aim of appeasing the opponent.[42] A few of the scientists however, have approached the problem without these limitations, and have therefore been able to make pertinent comments.[43]

To summarize the survey of current opinion on the philosophy of science, it can be said that for the most part philosophy, and in fact the general use of intelligence itself, have been surrendered to science. Rather than remain the judge and critic of scientific methods and discoveries, philosophy has become a reflection of science. There are of course the continental philosophical schools of existentialism and phenomenology, which, however, have had little effect on the scientific movement.[44] The phenomenological interpretation of science has as yet had little influence. Existentialism essentially cuts away the relations of man with nature and is little concerned with scientific questions. There are, amidst this scene, those who seek to demonstrate the limitations of science and others who explore with genuine interest the problems of the encounter between science, philosophy and religion. But throughout this complex scene the single factor that is nearly everywhere present is the lack of a metaphysical knowledge, of a *scientia sacra* which alone can determine the degrees of reality and of science. Only this knowledge can reveal the significance, symbolic and spiritual, of the ever more complex scientific theories and discoveries themselves which in the absence of this knowledge appear as sheer facts opaque and cut off from truths of a higher order.[45]

In as much as we are concerned with the spiritual aspect of the crisis of the encounter between man and nature, it is also of importance to discuss briefly the views of Christian theologians and thinkers on this subject, in addition to those of the philosophers of science noted above. It must be said at the outset that there has been singular neglect of this domain among Christian theologians, particularly Protestants. Most of the leading theological trends have dealt with man and history, and have concentrated on the question of the redemption of man as an isolated individual rather than on the redemption of all things. The theology of P. Tillich is centred on the problem of ultimate concern with the ground of being that encompasses the sacred and the profane and turns more to the existential role of man in history and his position as an isolated being before God rather than as a part of creation and within the cosmos itself considered as a hierophany. Even more removed from this question are the theologians like K. Barth and E. Brunner, who have drawn an iron wall around the world of nature.[46] They believe that nature cannot teach man anything about God and is therefore of no theological and spiritual interest.[47] As for the de-mythologizers like R. Bultmann, rather than penetrate into the inner meaning of myth as symbol of a transcendent reality which concerns the relation between man and God in history as well as in the cosmos, they, too, neglect the spiritual significance of nature, and reduce it to the status of a meaningless artificial background for the life of modern man.

Nevertheless there are a few who have realized the importance of nature as a background for religious life, and a religious science of nature as a necessary element in the integral life of a Christian.[48] They have understood the need to believe that the creation displays the mark of the Creator in order to be able to have a firm faith in religion itself.[49]

The day has passed when it was believed that science, in its ever continuing onward march pushes back the walls of theology, whose immutable principles appear from the view of a sentimental dynamism as rigid and petrified dogma, at least in many leading academic circles.[50] There are scientists who realize and respect the importance of the discipline of theology, while certain Christian theologians have asserted that the modern scientific view, because of its break with the closed mechanistic conception of classical physics, is more congenial to the Christian point of view.[51] This argument has in fact been advanced in so many quarters that people have begun to forget that the secularized world-view of modern science, once taken out of the hand of the professional scientist and presented to the public, places a great obstacle before the religious understanding of things.

Although in a sense the very destruction of a monolithic, mechanistic conception of the world has given a certain 'breathing space' to other views, the popularization of scientific theories and technology today has deprived men even more of a direct contact with nature and a religious conception of the world. 'Our Father which art in heaven' becomes incomprehensible to a person deprived by industrialized society of the patriarchal authority of a father and for whom heaven has lost its religious significance and ceased to be any 'where', thanks to flights of cosmonauts. It is only with respect to the theoretical relation between science and religion that one can say in a way that the modern scientific view is less incompatible with Christianity than the scientific views of the eighteenth and nineteenth centuries.

Not forgetting the transient character of scientific theories,

certain other Christian writers have warned against the facile
and all too easy harmony between religion and science in which
superficial comparisons are made between the two domains. All
too often the principles and tenets of religion, which are transcendent and immutable, are presented as being in conformity with
the latest findings of science, again following the well-known
tendency of reducing the greater to the lesser.[52] Furthermore, by
the time this process of conforming theology to current scientific
theories is carried out and religion is made 'reasonable' by
appearing as 'scientific', the scientific theories themselves have
gone out of vogue. In this domain one can at least say that among
a small but significant group there is a reaction against the
simplistic attitude prevalent in certain quarters in the nineteenth
century, although on the mass level there is much more retreat
of religion before what appears as scientific than in any previous
age.

Yet other writers have emphasized the close relation between
Christianity and science by pointing out that many of the fundamental assumptions of science such as belief in the orderliness
of the world, the intelligibility of the natural world and the
reliability of human reason depend upon the religious and more
particularly Christian view of a world created by God in which
the Word has become incarnated.[53] Some have related the problem of unity and multiplicity in nature to the Trinity in Christianity[54] while others have insisted that only Christianity has, in a
positive sense, made science possible.[55] But in all such cases one
wonders at the total validity of this assertion if one takes into
consideration the existence of sciences of nature in other civilizations (particularly Islam). These sciences insist on unity rather
than trinity. Further, we must consider the havoc modern science
and its applications have brought about within the world of
Christianity itself.

More specifically, the relation between subject and object as
held in modern science is said to derive from the relation between the spirit and the flesh in Christianity.[56] The order of the
Universe is identified with the Divine Mind,[57] and the scientist

33

is said to be discovering the mind of God in his scientific pursuits.[58] Scientific method itself has been called a Christian method of discovering God's mind.[59]

Of more central concern to our problem is the attempt of a few theologians, moving against the tide of the general modern trends of theology, to bring to life once again the sacramental character of all creation and to return to things the sacred nature of which recent modes of thought have deprived them. The importance of the created world as a sacrament revealing a dimension of religious life has been reasserted by this group,[60] and the forgotten truth that from the Christian point of view incarnation implies the sacramental nature of material things, without in any way destroying the causal nexus between things, has already been pointed out.[61] It has been re-affirmed that the only relation between the spiritual and the material which can in a deep sense be called Christian[62] is one in which the outward and material aspect of things acts as a vehicle for the inward, spiritual grace indwelling in all things, by virtue of their being created by God.[63] In order for God to be Creator and also eternally Himself, His Creation must be sacramental both to His creatures and to Himself.[64]

In the writings of this small group of theologians who have devoted some attention to the question of man's relation with nature, the revealed aspect of all the Universe has been brought out. If creation were not in some way revealed there would be no revelation possible.[65] Likewise, all creation must somehow share in the act of redemption in the same way as all creation is affected by the corruption and sin of man as asserted by St Paul in the *Epistle to the Romans* (Chapter VIII). The total salvation of man is possible when not only man himself but all creatures are redeemed.[66]

This point of view propounded above, which could have the profoundest significance in modern man's relation to nature, has however, rarely been understood and accepted. Even those who have devoted themselves most to a sacramental theology have, for the most part, failed to apply it to the world of nature. As a result, those who still feel and understand the meaning of the sacred, at least in religious rites, fail to extend it to the realm of nature. The sacramental or symbolic view of nature—if we understand symbol in its true sense—has not been in general propagated by modern schools of Christian theology. In fact the reverse holds true. In as much as the prevalent point of emphasis has been the redemption of the individual and disregard for the 'redemption of creation', most of modern religious thought has helped to secularize nature and has bent backwards to surrender to the dicta of science in the natural domain.

In discussing views of Christian authors on the sciences of nature, one cannot fail to mention the school of Neo-Thomism which has challenged the claim to totality and exclusiveness of scientific methods and has applied rigorous logical criteria to them.[67] The main tenet of the Neo-Thomist position has been to show that science is limited by its methods and cannot apply itself to a solution of metaphysical problems. It is not permissible to use the same methods and to proceed in the same manner in the domains of science and metaphysics. For, to quote St Thomas, 'It is a sin against intelligence to want to proceed in an identical manner in the typically different domains—physical, mathematical, and metaphysical—of speculative knowledge'.[68]

The knowledge of the whole Universe does not lie within the competence of science[69] but of metaphysics. Moreover, the principles of metaphysics remain independent of the sciences and cannot in any way be disproved by them.[70] One must realize the different forms of knowledge and place each within its own bounds. In fact the most important result of the Neo-Thomist view has not been so much to provide a new spiritual interpretation of nature and to return to it its sacred and symbolic character as to provide a philosophy of nature for science and to show through philosophical arguments the limitations existing within the scientific approach. It has been to safeguard the independence of theology and metaphysics from experimental sciences.[71] Whatever its shortcomings through being too rationalistic and not symbolic and metaphysical enough in the true sense, this school has at least affirmed and asserted a simple truth which is being forgotten more and more today, namely that the critical faculty of intelligence and of reason cannot be surrendered to the findings of an experimental science which that reason itself has made possible.

If one glances over the whole field of the relation between science, philosophy and theology, as we have done in a scanty and summary fashion, one becomes immediately aware of the lack of common ground between these three domains. Metaphysical doctrine, or that gnosis which alone can be the meeting ground of science and religion, has been forgotten, and as a result the hierarchy of knowledge has crumbled into a confused mass in which the segments are no longer organically united. Whereas philosophy has either recapitulated and surrendered itself to science or reacted totally against it, theology has either refused to consider the domain of nature and its sciences or has in turn adopted step by step the findings and methods of the sciences with the aim of creating a synthesis. This has often been as shallow as it has been transient. Moreover, a misunderstanding between the modern sciences of nature and a knowledge of the natural order which is of theological and spiritual significance has led to endless controversies and misunderstandings.[72]

For this very reason, and also despite all the activity in the natural sciences, there is today no philosophy of nature. While the medieval science of physics, which was indeed a natural philosophy, has become one science among other natural sciences, nothing has taken its place as the background of all the particular sciences of nature. Although the need for a philosophy of nature is felt even by some physicists (and many turn to the history of science precisely in order to receive inspiration for methods and philosophies which could be of aid in modern science), there still exists no generally accepted philosophy of nature, despite the philosophies proposed by several modern thinkers such as Whitehead and Maritain.[73]

One can say with even greater regret that there is also no theology of nature which could satisfactorily provide a spiritual bridge between man and nature. Some have realized the necessity of harmonizing Christian theology and natural philosophy to provide a theology of nature,[74] but such a task has not been accomplished, and cannot be so, until theology is understood in the intellectual light of the early Church Fathers, the Christian metaphysicians of the Middle Age, such as Erigena and Eckhart, or in the sense of the theosophy of Jacob Böhme. As long as by theology is understood a rational defence of the tenets of the faith, there is no possibility of a real theology of nature, no way of penetrating into the inner meaning of natural phenomena and making them spiritually transparent. Only the intellect can penetrate inwardly; reason can only explain.

This lack of sense of the transparency of things, of intimacy with nature as a cosmos that conveys to man a meaning that concerns him, is of course due to the loss of the contemplative and symbolist spirit which sees symbols rather than facts. The near disappearance of gnosis, as understood in its true sense as a unitive and illuminative knowledge, and its replacement by sentimental mysticism and the gradual neglect of apophatic and metaphysical theology in favour of a rational theology, are all effects of the same event that has taken place within the souls of men. The symbolic view of things is for the most part forgotten in the West and survives only among peoples of far away regions,[75] while the majority of modern men live in a de-sacralized world of phenomena whose only meaning is either their quantitative relationships expressed in mathematical formulae that satisfy the scientific mind, or their material usefulness for man considered as a two legged animal with no destiny beyond his earthly existence. But for man as an immortal being they bear no direct message. Or rather it can be said that they still bear the message but there is no longer the appropriate faculty to decipher it.

There seems to be in this movement from the contemplative to the passionate, from the symbolist to the factual mentality, a fall in the spiritual sense corresponding to the original fall of man. In the same way that Adam's fall from Paradise implies that creation, which had until then been innocent and friendly and also inward, thus became hostile and also externalized, so does the change of attitude between pre-modern and modern man *vis-à-vis* nature imply a further stage in this alienation. The I-thou relation is destroyed to become the I-it and no amount of the pejorative use of such terms as 'primitive', 'animistic' or 'pantheistic' can make one forget the loss implied in this change of attitude. In this new fall man has lost a paradise as a compensation for which he has discovered a new earth full of apparent but illusory riches.[76] He has lost the paradise of a symbolic world of meaning to discover an earth of facts which he is able to observe and manipulate at his will. But in this new role of a 'deity upon earth' who no longer reflects his transcendent archetype, he is in dire danger of being devoured by this very earth over which he seems to wield complete dominion unless he is able to regain a vision of that paradise he has lost.

For meanwhile the totally quantitative conception of nature which thanks to technology has begun to dominate all of life is gradually displaying cracks in its walls. Some are joyous about this event and believe it is the occasion of a reassertion of the spiritual view of things. But as a matter of fact most often the cracks are filled by the most negative 'psychic residues' and the practices of the 'occult sciences' which, once cut off from the grace of a living spirituality, become the most insidious of influences and are much more dangerous than materialism.[77] They are the water that dissolves rather than the earth that solidifies. Yet, these are not the 'waters above' but the 'waters below', to use the very significant Biblical symbolism. It is far from accidental that in most pseudo-spiritualist circles much is made of the synthesis of science and religion into a 'new spiritual order' as if man could create a ladder to heaven by himself, or, to speak in Christian terms, as if man could unite with the Christ nature unless the Christ nature had itself become man.

What is needed is a filling of the cracks in the wall of science by the light from above not by the darkness from below. Science must be integrated into a metaphysics from above so that its undisputed facts could also gain a spiritual significance.[78] And

38

because it is imperative, the need for such an integration is felt in many quarters[79] and many people with a degree of perspicacity look beyond the dangerous psycho-physical syntheses of today to which is usually added a spice of pseudo-Oriental 'wisdom'. A real synthesis would remain true to the deepest principles of the Christian revelation and the most rigorous demands of intelligence. This task can only be accomplished by re-discovering the spiritual meaning of nature. This discovery is itself dependent upon the remembrance of the most intellectual and metaphysical aspects of the Christian tradition which have been forgotten in so many circles today, along with awareness of the historical and intellectual causes that have brought about the present impasse. That is why we must first turn to consider certain phases in the history of science and philosophy in the West, as it is related to the Christian tradition, before turning to a discussion of metaphysical and cosmological principles in this tradition and in the traditions of the East traditions which can act as an aid to recollection for those within the world view of Christianity.

NOTES TO CHAPTER I

1. 'The cosmic liturgy, the mystery of nature's participation in the Christological drama, have become inaccessible to Christians living in a modern city. The religious experience is no longer open to the cosmos. In the last analysis, it is a strictly private experience; salvation is a problem that concerns man and his god; at most, man recognizes that he is responsible not only to God but also to history. But in these man-God-history relationships there is no place for the cosmos. From this it would appear that, even for a genuine Christian, the world is no longer felt as the work of God.' M. Eliade, *The Sacred and the Profane, the Nature of Religion*, New York, 1959, p. 179.

2. Many criticisms have appeared during the past two or three decades by naturalists, philosophers, social scientists, architects and men of other professions concerning the danger of domination over nature for man himself. The writings of Lewis Mumford and Joseph Wood Krutch represent two well known, but very different kinds of this type of literature which in a way

echo in quite altered conditions the concerns of William Morris and John Ruskin a century ago.

3. 'Experience of a radically desacralized nature is a recent discovery; moreover, it is an experience accessible only to a minority in modern societies, especially to scientists. For others, nature still exhibits a charm, a mystery, a majesty in which it is possible to decipher traces of ancient religious values.' Eliade, *op. cit.*, p. 151.

4. 'In a certain, external sense it may be said that the great social and political evil of the West is mechanization, for it is the machine which most directly engenders the great evils from which the world today is suffering. The machine is, generally speaking, characterized by the use of iron, of fire and of invisible forces. To talk about a wise use of machines, of their serving the human spirit, is utterly chimerical. It is in the very nature of mechanization to reduce men to slavery and to devour them entirely, leaving them nothing human, nothing above the animal level, nothing above the collective level. The kingdom of the machine followed that of iron, or rather gave to it its most sinister expression. Man, who created the machine, ends by becoming its creature.' F. Schuon, *Spiritual Perspectives and Human Facts* (trans. D. M. Matheson), London, 1953, p. 21.

5. 'What needs to be understood, however, is that happiness depends on the preliminary acceptance of a number of unpalatable facts. Chief among those facts is the practical knowledge, as distinct from any theory, of what makes for happiness. This knowledge is especially hard to come by for us of the West, conditioned as we are to making large demands on our environment, and to entertain the illusion that to raise the standard of living is equivalent to nourishing the human spirit.' Dom A. Graham, *Zen Catholicism, a Suggestion*, New York, 1963, p. 38. The same applies today to all of those affected by the psychosis of progress on whatever continent they might live.

6. See J. Sittler, *The Ecology of Faith*, Philadelphia, 1961, p. 22. The same author writes (p. 23): 'The entire experience of the peoples of America has created and nurtured a world view which stands over against the world view of the Bible in sharpest contrast possible.'

7. On this question see the masterly analysis of M. Pallis in *The Way and the Mountain*, London, 1960, Chapter I.

8. '... no longer is it human intellect but machines—or physics, or chemistry or biology—which decide what man is, what intelligence is, what truth is. Under these conditions man's mind more and more depends on the "climate" produced by its own creations. .'. . It is then science and machines which in their turn create man and if such an expression may be ventured, they also "create God" for the void thus left by dethroning God cannot remain empty, the reality of God and his imprint in human nature require a usurper of

divinity, a false absolute which can fill the nothingness of an intelligence robbed of its substance.' F. Schuon, *Understanding Islam* (trans. D. M. Matheson), London, 1963, pp. 32-3.

'Values which we accept today as permanent and often as self-evident have grown out of the Renaissance and the Scientific Revolution. The arts and the sciences have changed the values of the Middle Ages. . . . ' J. Bronowski, *Science and Human Values*, New York, 1965, p. 51.

9. 'Man has abused his trusteeship in God's world. He has employed his scientific knowledge to exploit nature rather than to use it wisely in accordance with God's Will.' G. D. Yarnold, *The Spiritual Crisis of the Scientific Age*, New York, 1959, p. 168.

10. 'Modern science is well equipped to provide certain kinds of information, but it denies itself the possibility of interpreting that information; the task of doing so is therefore left to the play of opinion, individual or collective, informed or ignorant. Its cardinal error therefore resides in its claim to be science itself, the only possible science, the only science there is.' Lord Northbourne, 'Pictures of the Universe', *Tomorrow*, Autumn, 1964, p. 275.

'. . . before the separation of science and the acceptance of it as the sole valid way of apprehending nature, the vision of God in nature seems to have been the normal way of viewing the world, nor could it have been marked as an exceptional experience.' F. Sherwood Taylor, *The Fourfold Vision*, London, 1945, p. 91.

11. This fact has been often affirmed by scientists themselves. For example, concerning the popular misunderstanding of the theory of relativity R. Oppenheimer writes: 'The philosophers and popularizers who have mistaken relativity for the doctrine of relativism have construed Einstein's great works as reducing the objectivity, firmness, and consonance to law of the physical world, whereas it is clear that Einstein has seen in his theories of relativity a further confirmation of Spinoza's view that it is man's highest function to know and understand the objective world and its laws.' R. Oppenheimer, *Science and the Common Understanding*, London, 1954, pp. 2-3.

12. '*L'équilibre du monde et des créatures dépend de l'équilibre entre l'homme et Dieu, donc de notre connaissance et notre volonté à l'égard de l'Absolu. Avant de demander ce qui doit faire l'homme, il faut savoir ce qu'il est.*' F. Schuon, 'Le commandement suprême', *Etudes Traditionnelles*, Sept.-Oct. 1965, p. 199.

13. 'It could be said that the very structure of the cosmos keeps memory of the celestial supreme being alive. It is as if the gods had created the world in such a way that it could not but reflect their existence; for no world is possible without verticality, and that dimension alone is enough to evoke transcendence.' M. Eliade, *op. cit.*, p. 129.

14. 'For religious man, nature is never only "natural"; it is always fraught

with religious·value. This is easy to understand, for the cosmos is a divine creation; coming from the hands of the gods, the world is impregnated with sacredness.' *Ibid.*, p. 116.

15. '. . . our knowledge (of cosmic phenomena) must be either symbolically true or physically adequate; in the second case it must retain for us a symbolic intelligibility, for without this all science is vain and harmful.' F. Schuon, *Light on the Ancient Worlds* (trans. Lord Northbourne), London, 1965, p. 105.

16. For a profound analysis of this question in all its aspects see R. Guénon, *The Reign of Quantity and the Signs of the Times* (trans. Lord Northbourne), London, 1953.

17. 'Modern science therefore asks us to sacrifice a good part of that which makes for us the reality of the world, and offers us in exchange mathematical schemes of which the only advantage is to help us to manipulate matter on its own plane, which is that of quantity.' T. Burckhardt, 'Cosmology and Modern Science', *Tomorrow*, Summer 1964, p. 186.

18. 'It could be demonstrated too that science, although in itself neutral—for facts are facts—is none the less a seed of corruption and annihilation in the hands of man, who in general has not enough knowledge of the underlying nature of Existence to be able to integrate—and thereby to neutralize—the facts of science in a total view of the world.' Schuon, *op. cit.*, p. 38.

19. '. . . all genuine cosmology is attached to a divine revelation, even if the object considered and the mode of its expression are situated apparently outside the message this revelation brings.

'Such is the case for instance, of Christian cosmology, the origin of which appears at first sight somewhat heterogeneous, since it refers on the one hand to the Biblical account of creation even while being based, on the other hand, on the heritage of the Greek cosmologists.' T. Burckhardt, 'Cosmology and Modern Science', *Tomorrow*, Summer, 1964, p. 182.

20. See for example E. C. Mascall, *Christian Theology and Natural Science*, London, 1956, Chapter IV.

21. 'Modern science will never reach that matter which is at the basis of this world. But between the qualitatively differentiated world and undifferentiated matter there lies something like an intermediate zone: This is chaos. The sinister dangers attendant on atomic fission are but a pointer indicating the frontier of chaos and of dissolution.' T. Burckhardt, 'Cosmology and Modern Science', p. 190.

22. This fact has of course been realized by certain historians of science and philosophy such as E. A. Burtt in his *Metaphysical Foundations of Modern Physical Science*, London, 1925; and A. Koyré in his many masterly works

The Problem

on Renaissance and seventeenth-century science, but it is none the less too often forgotten by a large number of philosophers and historians of science.

23. 'Anyone familiar with contemporary writing and talking knows that people are readier to accept physics as true and to use it to construct a "philosophy" than to investigate the method of physics, its presuppositions and their philosophical basis.' E. F. Caldin, *The Power and Limits of Science, a Philosophical Study*, London, 1949, p. 42.

24. See for example, M. White, *The Age of Analysis*, New York, 1955; A. W. Levi, *Philosophy and the Modern World*, Bloomington, 1959; Ch. Gillispie, *The Edge of Objectivity*, Princeton, 1960, and A. Danto and S. Morgenbesser (ed.), *Philosophy of Science*, New York, 1960.

25. Concerning the Vienna circle and the school of positivism see, Ph. Frank, *Modern Science and its Philosophy*, Cambridge, 1950, and Levi, *op. cit.*

26. See his essay, 'Science, Philosophy and Faith', in *Science, Philosophy and Religion, a Symposium*, New York, 1941, p. 166. Concerning the Vienna School he writes, 'The essential error of this school is to confuse that which is true (with certain restrictions) of the *science of phenomena*, and that which is true of *all science* and of all *knowledge* in general, of all scientific knowing. It is to apply universally to all human knowledge that which is valid only in one of its particular spheres. This leads to an absolute negation of metaphysics, and the arrogant pretension to deny that metaphysical assertions have any meaning.' pp. 169-70. He describes this attitude to 'The positivistic superstition concerning positive science'. p. 170.

27. See particularly his *De l'explication dans les sciences*, 2 vols., Paris, 1921.

28. This tendency to speak of 'universes of inquiry' and opposition to any 'unified world hypothesis' derived from the sciences is also emphasized by J. B. Conant in his *Modern Science and Modern Man*, New York, 1952, especially pp. 84 ff.

As for the 'operational' philosophy of science see P. Bridgman, *Logic of Modern Physics*, New York, 1927.

29. See H. Poincaré, *Science and Hypothesis*, New York, 1952, particularly Chapters IX and X; and his *La Valeur de la science*, Paris, 1948. Also, P. Duhem, 'Essai sur la notion de théorie physique de Platon à Galilée', *Annales de philosophie chrétienne*, Paris, 1908; *Origines de la statique*, 2 vols., Paris, 1905-6; and *The Aim and Structure of Physical Theory* (trans. Ph. Wiener), Princeton, 1954.

Although some have interpreted Mach's position as claiming that it deals with concepts rather than objective facts, the positivists claim that the main message of his main works *Beiträge zur Analyse der Empfindungen* and *Die*

43

Mechanik in ihrer Entwickelung is to remove all traces of metaphysics from science and thereby unify it, a unification of science through elimination of metaphysics! One wonders how it is possible to mistake unity and uniformity and attempt to unify any domain of multiplicity without a principle that transcends that multiplicity. Concerning Mach see C. B. Weinberg, *Mach's Empirio-Pragmatism in Physical Science*, New York, 1937.

30. As Poincaré puts it, '*Tout ce qui n'est pas penseé est le pur néant.*' *La Valeur de la science*, p. 276. This is a clear indication of the subjectivism so characteristic of modern thought because the '*pensée*' in question here is not in any way attached to the objective Intellect but is purely subjective and changeable like the external nature of man itself.

31. See E. Cassirer, *The Problem of Knowledge* (trans. W. Woglom and C. Hendel), New Haven, 1950; *Substance and Function*, La Salle, 1923; and H. Morgenau, *The Nature of Physical Reality*, New York, 1950.

32. F. S. C. Northrop, *The Meeting of East and West,* New York, 1946; and *Man, Nature and God, a Quest for Life's Meaning*, New York, 1962.

33. 'One of the most important results of the philosophy of natural science of our own day is its demonstration that the sensuously and aesthetically immediate natural history knowledge of nature which Goethe emphasized, and the theoretically designated, experimeritally verified, mathematical knowledge of nature, which Newton and Kant emphasized are both equally ultimate, irreducible and real.' *Man, Nature and God*, pp. 153–4.

Concerning the views of Kant and Goethe regarding nature see E. Cassirer, *Rousseau-Kant-Goethe*, Princeton, 1945.

34. 'Nature is a universally lawful organism. It is a cosmos, not a chaos. . . .' *Man, Nature and God*, p. 229.

35. See J. Jeans, *Physics and Philosophy*, Cambridge, 1942; and *The New Background of Science*, New York, 1933; A. Eddington, *The Philosophy of Physical Science*, New York, 1958 and especially his *The Nature of the Physical World*, Cambridge, 1932, which has been probably more widely influential than any work of its kind written by a modern scientist.

In contrast to Eddington certain physicists have turned to physics itself for proofs of the existence and nature of God. See for example E. Whittaker, *Space and Spirit, Theories of the Universe and the Arguments for the Existence of God*. London, 1946.

36. See especially A. N. Whitehead, *Process and Reality*, New York, 1929; *The Concept of Nature*, Cambridge, 1920; and *Science and the Modern World*, New York, 1948.

Whitehead decries the poverty of the scientific conception of nature that excludes the realities of religion and art and seeks to construct an all pervasive view of nature. 'Thus, the science of nature stands opposed to the presuppositions of humanism. Where some conciliation is attempted, it often assumes some sort of mysticism. But in general there is no conciliation', *Nature and Life*, Chicago, 1934, p. 4.

37. '. . . The premises of science cannot be explicitly formulated, and can be found authentically manifested only in the practice of science, as maintained by the tradition of science.' M. Polanyi, *Science, Faith and Society*, Chicago, 1964, p. 85.

38. 'So that science, whether old or new, can never without self-contradiction, prove an idealistic thesis and allow itself to be a base for attacking an empirico-realistic standpoint. Idealistic thinkers ought to seek other ways to fulfil their noble mission. But then science cannot be used to back up a materialistic thesis either.' P. J. Chaudhury, *The Philosophy of Science*, Calcutta, 1955.

39. An outstanding modern physicist, W. Heisenberg writes: 'Like the regular elementary bodies of Plato's philosophy, the elementary particles of modern physics are defined by the mathematical conditions of symmetry; they are not eternal and invariable and are therefore hardly what can be called "real" in the true sense of the word. Rather, they are simple representations of those fundamental mathematical structures that are arrived at in the attempts to keep subdividing matter; they represent the content of fundamental laws of nature. For modern natural science there is no longer in the beginning the material object, but form, mathematical symmetry. And since mathematical symmetry is in the last analysis an intellectual content, we could say in the words of Goethe's Faust; "In the beginning was the word, the logos." To know this logos in all particulars and with complete clarity with respect to the fundamental structure of matter is the task of present-day atomic physics. . . .' W. Heisenberg, M. Born, E. Schrödinger, P. Anger; *On Modern Physics*, New York, 1961, p. 19. Although this statement is to a certain degree true in that all natural laws and the intelligible comprehension of their content come from the Logos, surely it is mistaking the reflection with the thing itself to identify the intellectual content of mathematical symmetry with the Logos itself. The significance of this symmetry exists and is felt by physicists but only metaphysics can show that it is an application of a more universal principle. Without metaphysics one falls again into the error of reducing the higher to the lower, the Word to mathematical intelligibility of the form of material objects.

40. Concerning the doctrine of identity which offers both a higher ethical content and a deeper religious consolation than materialism, E. Schrödinger writes, 'Materialism offers neither; though there are many people who convince themselves that the idea which astronomy gives us of myriads of suns

with, perhaps, inhabitable planets, and of a multitude of galaxies, each with myriads of such, and ultimately of a probably finite universe, affords us a sort of ethical and religiously consoling vision, mediated to our senses by the indescribable panorama of the starry heavens on a clear night. To me personally all that is maya, albeit maya in a very interesting form, exhibiting laws of great regularity. It has little to do with my eternal inheritance (to express myself in a thoroughly medieval fashion).' E. Schrödinger, *My View of the World*, Cambridge, 1964, p. 107.

41. 'Skepticism has been the privilege of a few men of learning who could survive because around them stood a world of faith unshaken. Today, skepticism has entered the masses, and has rocked the foundations of their order of life. It is the men of learning who are frightened now.' C. F. von Weizsäcker, *The History of Nature*, Chicago, 1949, p. 177.

42. 'Practically all the attempts that have been made to bridge the gap between theology and the sciences have come from the theological side.' Yarnold, *The Spiritual Crisis of the Scientific Age*, pp. 54–5.

43. The type of work by scientists to which we refer here is exemplified by C. F. von Weizsäcker's, *The Relevance of Science*, London, 1964.

See also the writings of the botanist A. Arber especially her *The Manifold and the One*, London, 1957, containing an extensive bibliography on the traditional conception of nature.

44. There have been certain works by phenomenologists which concern science but they have not until now received much attention from scientists themselves. See for example E. Ströker, *Philosophische Untersuchungen zum Raum*, Frankfurt am Main, 1965, on the notion of space as it pertains to philosophy, physics and mathematics. Also see M. Scheler, *Man's Place in Nature*, (trans. H. Meyerhoff), Boston, 1961, the last of Scheler's works, in which the unified view of man and the world about him characteristic of phenomenology is set forth.

For a summary of the interaction of phenomenology and science especially as it concerns the position of man in the world see A. Tymieniecka, *Phenomenology and Science in Contemporary European Thought*, New York, 1962.

45. 'Thus the picture of the universe presented by modern science becomes ever more complex, obscure and remote from the natural picture. Nevertheless, independently of any question as to its relative validity, it exists as an influential factor in contemporary thought; that being the case it is part of ourselves and part of the universe. Its ultimate cause cannot therefore be other than the ultimate cause of all things, and like all things, including the natural picture, the scientific picture can be seen as a symbol of its cause, that is to say, as a partial reflection of that cause on the plane of appearances. But when its outward form alone is considered that form becomes a more or

less impenetrable veil, hiding the causes although if its symbolical significance can be discovered, the same can reveal the cause.' Lord Northbourne, 'Pictures of the Universe', p, 275.

46. One of the followers of this school, K. Heim, has shown some interest in science as seen by his *Christian Faith and Natural Sciencè,* New York, 1953. But the deepest problems involved have been hardly delved into especially as far as the question of the symbolic significance of natural phenomena and their religious meaning are concerned.

47. It might be pointed out in passing that surely it is not accidental that Barthian theology shows both a disregard for the study of nature and of comparative religion. Both the cosmos and other religions thus appear as a 'natural' domain cut off from the domain of grace with which Christian theology should be concerned.

48. See for example, J. Oman, *The Natural and the Supernatural,* Cambridge, 1936.

49. 'Only a thoroughgoing belief that "the things that are made" do, in spite of the Fall and its consequences, manifest the true nature of their Maker can give any foundation for a reasonable faith.' C. E. Raven, *Natural Religion and Christian Theology,* Cambridge, 1953, p. 137.

50. We mean the point of view so characteristic of the writings of the turn of the century such as A. D. White, *A History of the Warfare of Science and Theology in Christendom,* 2 vols., New York, 1960.

51. 'But it is at once evident that the general outline of the structure of the universe, as presented by science today, is far more congenial to the theistic hypothesis, as we have been considering it, than were the scientific theories prevalent in the eighteenth and nineteenth centuries.' W. Temple, *Nature, Man and God,* New York, 1949, p. 474.

52. 'I can think of no greater disservice that could be done to the Christian religion than to tie it up with arguments based upon verbal confusions or with scientific views that are merely temporary.' Mascall, *Christian Theology and Natural Science,* p. 166.

53. See Smethurst, *Modern Science and Christian Belief,* pp. 17–18.
   'Only the full catholic Christian faith can supply both the necessary theological and philosophical beliefs as to the nature of the universe which are required to justify studying it by the scientific method, and also the impulse and inspiration which will impel men to undertake this study.' *Ibid.,* p. 20.

54. See for example R. G. Collingwood, *Essay on Metaphysics,* Oxford, 1940, p. 227.

55. 'I am convinced that Christianity alone made possible both positive

science and technics.' N. Berdyaev, *The Meaning of History*, London, 1935, p. 113.

56. See W. Temple, *Nature, Man and God*, p. 478, where the author adds that Christianity is able to dominate over matter precisely because in contrast to other religions such as Hinduism it is 'the most avowedly materialist of all the great religions'.

'I believe that the distance which in the modern mind exists between the subject and the object is a direct legacy of the Christian distance from the world.' von Weizäcker, *The History of Nature*, p. 190.

57. This point of view is particularly developed by G. F. Stout in his *God and Nature*, Cambridge, 1952

58. See for example Yarnold, *The Spiritual Crisis of the Scientific Age*, pp. 54 ff.

59. 'Thus, the scientific method should be regarded as one method which Christians employ to obtain a better understanding of the wisdom of God and the wonders of His Creation. . . .' Smethurst, *Modern Science and Christian Belief*, p. 71.

60. One is reminded of the saying of Oliver Chase, 'For mankind there are two unique sacraments which disclose the meaning and convey the experience of reality: They are the created Universe and the person of Jesus Christ' (quoted by Raven, *Natural Religion and Christian Theology*, p. 105). This is reminiscent of early American Protestant theologians like Jonathan Edwards who were concerned with the theological meaning of nature.

61. See A. N. Whitehead, *Science and the Modern World*, Chapter I.

62. 'It is not simply the relation of ground and consequent, nor of cause and effect, nor of thought and expression, nor of purpose and instrument, nor of end and means; but it is all of these at once. We need for it another name; and there is in some religious traditions an element which is, in the belief of adherents of those religions, so closely akin to what we want that we may most suitably call this conception of the relation of the eternal to history, of spirit to matter, the sacramental conception.' Temple, *Nature, Man and God*, pp. 481–2.

63. Through sacraments, 'The outward and visible sign is a necessary means for conveyance of the inward and spiritual grace'. *Ibid.*, p. 482.

64. 'His creation is sacramental of Himself to His creatures; but in effectually fulfilling that function it becomes sacramental of Him to Himself—the means whereby He is eternally that which eternally He is.' *Ibid.*, p. 495.

65. 'The world, which is the self-expressive utterance of the Divine Word, becomes itself a true revelation, in which what comes is not truth concerning God, but God Himself.' *Ibid.*, p. 493.

'Either all occurrences are in some degree revelations of God, or else there is no such revelation at all; for the conditions of the possibility of any revelation require that there should be nothing which is not revelation. Only if God is revealed in the rising of the sun in the sky can He be revealed in the rising of a son of man from the dead'; *ibid.*, p. 306.

66. 'The theatre of redemption is the theatre of creation.' J. Sittler, *The Ecology of Faith*, p. 25.

67. See for example the writings of J. Maritain, J. Weisheipl and A. G. Van Melsen, especially the latter's *The Philosophy of Nature*, Pittsburg, 1961; also V. E. Smith (ed.), *The Logic of Science*, New York, 1963, containing essays by M. Adler, J. A. Weisheipl and others on the neo-Thomistic philosophy of nature and science.

68. Quoted by J. Maritain in his essay, 'Science, Philosophy and Faith', in *Science, Philosophy and Religion, a Symposium*, p. 171.

69. 'But the depiction of the whole cosmos, in its complete complexity is a task that does not properly lie within the competence of Science.' F. R. S. Thompson, *Science and Common Sense*, London, 1937, p. 54.

70. '... in principle, theses of a genuinely metaphysical nature are not subject to verification by the senses, so that no amount of experimental research can ever dislodge them from their position.' H. J. Koren, *An Introduction to the Philosophy of Nature*, Pittsburgh, 1960, p. 181.

71. This can be seen particularly in the writings of a leading spokesman of this school, J. Maritain. See particularly his *Philosophy of Nature*, New York, 1947, and *The Degrees of Knowledge* (trans. B. Wall and M. Adamson), New York, 1938.

72. 'Indeed it is largely out of the misunderstanding between the order of nature and the field of science that our controversies have arisen.' Raven, *Natural Religion and Christian Theology, I, Science and Religion*, p. 6.

73. Putting Whitehead and his school aside and a few individual philosophers like Collingwood who have shown interest in nature, no other philosophical school has been as insistent on the necessity of a philosophy of nature and on trying to provide such a philosophy based on Thomism. Also phenomenology provides in itself a philosophy of nature but none of those schools have found wide or total acceptance.

74. See for example, Yarnold, *The Spiritual Crisis of the Scientific Age*, p. 23.

75. 'The feeling of the sanctity of nature survives today in Europe chiefly among rural populations, for it is among them that a Christianity lived as a cosmic liturgy still exists.' Eliade, *The Sacred and the Profane . . .*, p. 178.

76. 'This transition from objectivism to subjectivism reflects and repeats in

its own way the fall of **Adam and the loss of Paradise**; in losing a symbolist and contemplative perspective, founded both on impersonal intelligence and on the metaphysical transparency of things, man has gained the fallacious riches of the *ego*; the world of divine images has become a world of words. In all cases of this kind, heaven—or a heaven—is shut off from above us without our noticing the fact and we discover in compensation an earth long unappreciated, or so it seems to us, a homeland which opens its arms to welcome its children and wants to make us forget all lost Paradises. . . .' Schuon, *Light on the Ancient Worlds*, p. 29. See also Eliade, *op. cit.*, p. 213.

77. Concerning this subject see Guénon, *The Reign of Quantity . . .*, especially Chapter XXV, 'Fissures in the Great Wall'.

78. 'I have suggested that scientific explanation, "from below", must be supplemented by something far wider and deeper, interpretation, from above. Until that is accomplished our hold upon essential Christian truth is weak and often ineffectual.' Yarnold, *The Spiritual Crisis of the Scientific Age*, p. 7.

79. 'The division of labor in acquiring knowledge, although it begets new sciences, is yet a recognition of the unity and integrity of all knowledge and a challenge to expose it. This is a much different undertaking than trying to piece together as parts of a whole the specific results of specific sciences or using the results of one of them to shape the concerns of the others. Nature, not the wit of man, gives to knowledge its integral character. This suggests a science of nature which is neither physics nor chemistry and the like nor the social sciences and their like. . . .' F. J. E. Woodbridge, *An Essay on Nature*, New York, 1940, p. 58.

Chapter 2

The Intellectual and Historical Causes

A great deal of the blame for the neglect of other conceptions of science and failure to grasp the true significance of ancient and medieval cosmologies and other sciences of nature rests upon the manner in which these sciences are studied today. The investigation of the history of science, which during this century has become an important academic discipline, has concentrated more on glorifying modern science or searching for its historic roots than in making a study in depth of conceptions of nature in different civilizations and epochs of history or penetrating into the metaphysical significance of the ancient and medieval sciences. Most scholars in this field have turned their sole attention to those elements and factors in ancient and medieval or, for that matter, Renaissance science that resemble, anticipate or have influenced modern science.[1] In fact, modern science has been taken by most science historians as the only legitimate and possible form of science of nature, and all other cosmological sciences have been considered either as early anticipations of this form of science or as deviations which have hindered modern science. The use of the word "science" in English is particularly significant and indicative of the point of view in question.[2]

We do not, however, belittle the significance of the studies made in the domain of the history of science in which, through the historical approach, the roots of a particular science and its past formation are clarified. The pioneering work of such men as Berthelot, Mach, Duhem, Sarton, Tannery, Thorndike and others have contributed immensely to our understanding of the scientific activity of other ages. But few of these works can help in solving the problem of the modern crisis of the encounter of man and nature. This is because rather than become independent judges of ancient and medieval sciences and objective observers or even critics of modern science they have completely adopted the point of view that the only possible and legitimate form of science is the modern one.

There has been in the professional ranks of science historians, particularly before the nineteen-fifties, a singular neglect of the symbolic meaning of the ancient and medieval sciences and a tendency to read into older texts meanings and concepts proper to modern science. Many have written about the concepts of matter or motion in the ancient world as if in those days people held the same views about the physical world as the contemporary ones. Pre-Socratic philosophers have been hailed as forerunners of modern physicists as if the water of Thales were the water of modern chemistry; or the Babylonians are held as the first astronomers in the modern sense, while the religious significance of their astronomical observations is forgotten completely. No doubt Babylonian mathematics is a brilliant chapter in the history of mathematics but we wonder if it is 'scientifically' correct to speak of Babylonian science as if its only meaning were that which modern mathematicians understand by it. The symbolic significance of the seven planets, their motion and relation to the earthly domain is, for those who understand it, as exact as that part of Babylonian science which is treated as 'exact science' through standards placed upon it by modern scholars who hold a view totally alien to that of the Babylonians.

Alternatively, we could question whether Islamic science is only that element which contributed to the rise of modern science; or when we speak of medieval science whether we should concentrate only on those thirteenth- and fourteenth-century theologians and philosophers like Ockham, Oresme, Buridan, Grosseteste and others who anticipated the mathematical and physical works of Benedetti, Galileo and other founders of modern science. The existence of interest in dynamics and mechanics amongst late medieval nominalists is surely of importance, but with the same certainty we can also assert that this is not the whole of medieval science but is merely the view of modern historians of science as to what, in fact, medieval science was. If we wish to use the history of science beneficially to solve the acute problems modern science and its applications have brought about, we cannot be satisfied merely with the current method of studying the history of science. We must also study the sciences of nature of other civilizations and periods, independently of their contribution, or lack of it, to modern science. We must consider these sciences as being independent views about nature some of which may be of considerable aid in the solution of contemporary problems[3] and as providing a background for the criticism of certain aspects of modern science. It is in this light that we turn, therefore, to the history of science in the hope of discovering the intellectual and historical causes of the present situation.

The historical background of both science itself and Greek and Christian philosophy and theology are important for any present day discussion, because the individual as well as the culture in which he lives inevitably carry within them the deep roots of their past. The present day encounter of man and nature, and all the philosophical, theological and scientific problems connected with it, carry within themselves elements connected with Christian civilization[4] as well as with the civilization of Antiquity which Christianity came to replace. In order then to discover the deep causes of contemporary problems we are forced to return to the beginning and to consider those causes, both intellectual and historical, which still exist today.

The ancient Greeks possessed a cosmology similar to that of other Aryan peoples of Antiquity. The elements, and nature itself, were still inhabited by the Gods. Matter was alive with spirit and the spiritual and corporeal substances had not as yet become distinct. The rise of philosophy and science in the sixth century BC was not so much the discovery of a new realm as an attempt to fill a vacuum created by the fact that the Olympian Gods had deserted their earthly abode. The basic ideas of *phusis*, *dike, nomos* and the like which are fundamental to Greek science and philosophy are all terms of religious significance which have been gradually emptied of their spiritual substance.[5] The pre-Socratic philosophers, far from being early examples of modern naturalists and scientists, were still searching for the universal substance which is both spiritual and corporeal and they can be quite legitimately compared to the Hindu cosmologists of the school of Sāṃkhya. The water of Thales is not what flows in rivers and streams but is the psycho-spiritual substratum and principle of the physical world.

With the gradual increase in decadence of the Greek Olympian religion, more and more the substance of nature itself became divorced from its spiritual significance, and cosmology and physics tended toward naturalism and empiricism. In the same way that from the Orphic-Dionysian dimension of Greek religion there developed the Pythagorean-Platonic school of philosophy and mathematics, so from the body of Olympian religious concepts, emptied of their meaning, arose a physics and a natural philosophy which sought to fill the vacuum and to provide a coherent explanation for a world no longer inhabited by the gods.[6] The general movement was from symbolic interpretation of nature to naturalism, from contemplative metaphysics to rationalistic philosophy.

With the birth of Aristotle, philosophy as understood in the West began and as understood in the East terminated.[7] After Aristotle, rationalism as expressed in the Stoic, Epicurean and other late schools became prevalent in the Roman empire, a rationalism which however, contributed little to the natural sciences[8] directly and which showed little concern for the metaphysical and theological significance of the sciences. In Alexandria, however, mystical and religious schools of philosophy developed during a period of intense activity in the mathematical and physical sciences. It was here that Neoplatonic metaphysics, Neopythagorean mathematics and Hermeticism were developed and where the study of mathematical and natural sciences was often carried out in the matrix of a metaphysics that was aware of the symbolic and transparent nature of things. It is of significance that the immediate background of Western civilization, in its external and formal aspect, is Roman while that which Islam received from the Graeco-Hellenistic heritage comes mostly from Alexandria. Christianity, when it was called upon to save a civilization rather than a few souls, was faced with a world in which naturalism, empiricism and rationalism were rampant, where knowledge of a human order had become divinized and where an excessive attraction to nature seemed to the Christian eye a blasphemy that blinded men to the vision of God.

Christianity, therefore, reacted against this naturalism by emphasizing the boundary between the supernatural and the natural and by making the distinction between the natural and supernatural so strict as to come near to depriving nature of the inner spirit that breathes through all things. To save the souls of men in the particular atmosphere in which it found itself, Christianity had to forget and neglect, or at least belittle, the theological and spiritual significance of nature. Henceforth, the study of nature from a theological point of view did not occupy a central place in Western Christianity.[9]

To preserve a correct theology Christianity became opposed to the 'cosmic religion' of the Greeks, and some theologians called nature *massa perditionis*. In the dialogue between the Christian and the Greek, in which both sides were expressing an aspect of the truth but each a half truth, the Christian emphasized the nature of God, the human soul and salvation while the Greek emphasized the 'divine' quality of the cosmos and the 'supernatural' status of intelligence itself which enables man to know the universe.[10] Against this cosmology Christianity opposed its theology and against this emphasis upon knowledge, accented the path of love. To overcome the danger of rationalism divorced from gnosis it made knowledge the handmaid of faith and ignored the supernatural essence of natural intelligence within men. Only in this way was it able to save a civilization and to instill into a decadent world a new spiritual life; but in the process an alienation took place towards nature which has left its mark upon the subsequent history of Christianity. This is one of the deep-lying roots of the present crisis of modern man in his encounter with nature.

The character of Christianity as a way of love rather than as knowledge needs particular emphasis. In envisaging man as a will rather than an intelligence, Christianity has emphasized the pull of faith and love over knowledge and certitude. Illuminative knowledge or gnosis[11] has existed in Christianity but mostly on the periphery, especially as far as Western Christianity is concerned. Knowledge derived from intelligence without the aid of faith came to be considered as 'knowledge according to the flesh', in conformity with the Christian conception of man as an essentially warped will whose wound must be healed through the rite of Baptism. There was not that accent upon the supernatural essence of the intelligence and on that gnosis or illuminative knowledge which is at once the source and meeting ground of both faith and reason. The Greek gnostic saw in man's natural aptitude to know a means of reaching the Absolute Truth itself. It may also be added that Islam in the cadre of Abrahamic monotheism likewise made gnosis central and placed the accent not so much on the will of man, whose wound had to be healed, but on the intelligence which had only to be reminded through revelation of its supernatural essence.

In any case, because of its character as a way of love and the excessively naturalistic background in which it was called upon to fill the spiritual vacuum caused by the decadence of Graeco-Roman religions, Christianity drew a sharp line between the supernatural and the natural, or grace and nature. The official theology left the problem of nature as a positive domain in the religious life out of its central concern, especially after the formulation of the Creeds and the exteriorization of the esoteric way that is Christianity; this followed inevitably, since after its early days Christianity was called upon not only to save a selected few but a whole civilization that was falling apart. The gnostic element continued to exist, but only as a sideline development which periodically, through the history of Christianity, has manifested itself in different forms. It has been the one element which enabled Christianity to develop in the Middle Ages a cosmology of its own and to adapt to its needs those forms of cosmology and sciences of nature that were conformable to its perspective.

The relation between metaphysical and theological principles of a religious tradition such as Christianity and the cosmological sciences must be made clear. Either the cosmological sciences are based on, or drawn from the metaphysical sources of the religion itself, or they are adopted from an alien tradition but integrated into the perspective of the tradition in question. The traditional cosmological sciences—that whole series of sciences dealing with figures, numbers, forms, colours and correspondence between various orders of reality—can only be understood, and their symbolic significance discovered, in the light of a living spirituality. Without the light of a living tradition with its own metaphysics and theology the cosmological sciences become opaque and unintelligible. Seen in this light these sciences become shining crystals that illuminate the multiple phenomena of the Universe and make them intelligible and transparent.[12] It was in this way that both Islam and Christianity integrated Hermetic cosmology into their esoteric dimensions and gave it new life and significance.

The ambivalent source of Christian cosmology is seen in the fact that there, both Biblical or Hebrew cosmological concepts and Greek ones stand side by side. There is the Biblical cosmogony based on creation *ex-nihilo* and on a drama that occurs in time. Then there are the Greek cosmologies which occur in 'space' without regard for temporal and secular change, one in which time is cyclic and the world appears to lack a temporal beginning. Christianity adopted elements of both these cosmological views, and the long disputes among theologians and philosophers as to the creation or eternity of the world and the nature of time and space, reflect this dual origin of cosmology within the Christian perspective. It is this absorption of Graeco-Hellenistic elements into Western Christian civilization, both directly at the beginning of the Christian era and then again in the modified

form given to them by Islam during the Middle Ages, that made
possible the arts and sciences in the medieval period, and also
served as the background for the scientific revolution. One
should therefore always remember both the character of the
sciences of the Greek world as they came to be known by later
ages and the attitude and reaction of Christianity itself *vis-à-vis*
this heritage. Both are of basic importance in the attitude of
Western man toward nature in all subsequent periods of Western
history including the contemporary.

As Christianity grew from the religion of a few to the spiritual
life force of a humanity, and began to mould a civilization which
was distinctly Christian, it had to develop both its own art,
cosmology and sciences of the natural world.[13] If theologically
Christianity emphasized a rejection of the 'life of this world' and
a search for a kingdom which was not of this world, in its total
view of things it also had to possess the means of equating the
techniques of the artisans with Christian activity and the world
in which the Christian man lived with a Christian Universe. It
succeeded on both accounts, in creating both an artisanal tradition
that could construct the medieval cathedrals which are a micro-
cosmic model of the Christian cosmos, and a total science of the
visible Universe which depicted this Universe as a Christian one.
When man stands in a medieval cathedral he feels himself at the
centre of the world.[14] This could only be brought about through
the relation between sacred art and cosmology that existed in
medieval Christianity as it has in other traditions. The cathedral
recapitulates the cosmos and is its replica on the human plane in
the same way that the medieval city with its walls and gates is a
model of the bound medieval Universe.[15]

The science of natural objects and the techniques of making
things, or art in its most universal sense, were developed together
in the new Christian civilization, and both were integrated as a
hidden and secret knowledge into the esoteric dimensions of
Christianity. The popular knowledge of nature was based on
survivals of such works as the *Historia naturalis* of Pliny and

other late popular encyclopaedias, on the writings of Isadore of Seville, Gregory, Bede and similar medieval authors, and on elements of Platonic cosmology as derived from the *Timaeus* and often cited in the writings of some of the Fathers as well as by more popular writers. Yet the most profound elements of the Christian knowledge of nature and things natural were to be found in secret societies, guilds and associations connected with the esoteric aspect of Christianity. Whether unformulated, as among the guild of masons, or articulated as in the case of the secret association of the *Fedeli d'amore* to which Dante belonged, the sciences of nature and cosmology connected with this aspect of medieval Christian civilization represent the most profound aspects of the process of Christianization.

In order to achieve this end, Christianity integrated into its more inward dimensions elements of the Hermetic-Pythagorean cosmological sciences. The Pythagorean science of harmony, of numbers, geometric forms and colours, pervaded the science and art of the Middle Ages. So many of the medieval cathedrals, of which Chartres is an outstanding example, are a synthesis of medieval art and science in which the element of harmony is the guiding principle. The proportions of so many of these sacred structures are notes of music in stone.[16]

As for Hermeticism, it provided Christianity with a sacred science of material objects. The elemental materials of the natural world became so many building blocks which led the soul from the darkness of the *materia prima* to the luminosity of the intelligible world. The Hermetical and alchemical perspective, which in an articulate form entered into the Christian world through Islamic sources, extended the sacramental conception present in the Christian mass to the whole of nature. Through it, the artisan was able to transform the substance of the corporeal world about him so that it could possess and convey spiritual efficacy and significance.[17]

As we glance at the Middle Ages we see on the one hand a popular natural history imbued more and more with Christian values of an ethical order, as reflected in medieval books of animals, and on the other a science of nature associated closely with the craftsman's guilds. In the latter an operative knowledge of nature was primarily emphasized, while the theoretical knowledge remained for the most part unwritten or unformulated. Occasionally an intellectual expression would be given of this religious science of things and of the cosmos as a whole. This we find in the works of Dante and somewhat before him in the school of Chartres.

The type of science of nature which is profoundly Christian, both in its aims and its presuppositions, is however associated more with the contemplative and metaphysical dimension of Christianity than with the theological. In fact, the cosmological perspective can be integrated only into the metaphysical dimension of a tradition and not into the theological aspect as this term is usually understood. Theology is too rationalistic and man-orientated to be concerned with the spiritual essence and symbolism of cosmic phenomena, unless we understand by theology the apophatic and contemplative theology which is more metaphysical than rationalistic and philosophical. And so, with certain exceptions as in the case of Erigena or the school of Chartres, in theological circles little interest was taken in the symbolic and contemplative view of nature. It was left to St Francis of Assisi to express, within the bosom of Christian spirituality, the profoundest insights into the sacred quality of nature. A few northern European scientists and philosophers like Roger Bacon were to combine observation of nature with a mystical philosophy based on illumination, but this was more of an exception than a rule. Even later Franciscans like the great theologian St Bonaventure, who expressed the necessity of a *sapientia* as a background for *scientia*, were not particularly interested in the study of nature.

Into the world of early medieval Christianity, dominated by Augustinian theology, Dionysian angelology and a Christian cosmology drawn from Platonic, Pythagorean and Hermetic elements, there entered in the eleventh century a new form of learning from the Islamic world. Besides the spread of certain occult sciences like alchemy, and even esoteric contact between

Islam and Christianity through the Order of the Temple and other secret organizations[18], the main result of this contact was acquaintance with Peripatetic philosophy and science as it had been developed by the Muslims for several centuries.

Here, we are not concerned with how this transmission took place nor with the different sciences that became known through this process to the Latin world. Rather, we wish to turn to the effect of this new development in the general view of nature. The Muslims had for several centuries developed Peripatetic science and philosophy as well as mathematics, but at the same time the gnostic, illuminationist dimension associated with Sufism had been alive from the start and continued as the inner life force of this tradition.[19] In fact, Islam turned more and more to this direction during its later history.

In the Occident, however, the translation of Arabic works into Latin, which caused a major intellectual change from the eleventh to the thirteenth centuries, resulted gradually in the Aristotelianization of Christian theology. Rationalism came to replace the earlier Augustinian theology based on illumination and the contemplative view of nature was increasingly pushed aside as the gnostic and metaphysical dimension of Christianity became ever more stifled in an increasingly rationalistic environment.

A case in point is the career of the philosophy of Ibn Sînâ—the Latin Avicenna—the greatest of the Muslim Peripatetics in the West. To the present day Avicenna has continued to exert influence upon Islamic intellectual life. The later reviver of Peripatetic philosophy, Ibn Rushd or Averroes, however, exercised much less influence upon his co-religionists. In the West a somewhat misunderstood Averroes became, during the thirteenth century, the master of the Latin Averroists who were associated with pre-Christian learning. Yet Avicenna never gained enough disciples in the West to have even the honour of a school of 'Latin Avicennism' named after him.[20]

The Aristotelianism of Averroes was much more pure and radical than that of other Muslim philosophers, while Avicenna had combined this philosophy with the tenets of Islam and even developed later in life an 'Oriental philosophy' based on illumination.[21] The interpretation of Averroes in the West as an even more rationalistic philosopher than he actually was, and the lack of a systematic acceptance of Avicenna, are the best indication of the movement toward rationalism in the Christian world. This inclination is brought to light particularly when the situation in the Occident is compared with the intellectual life of its sister Islamic civilization during the same period. Through this process, theology came to replace metaphysics or rather rationalistic theology replaced the contemplative theology of earlier centuries. The result of this change was to become evident after an interim period of relative equilibrium.

The career of Avicennian cosmology is of particular pertinence in this development. For Avicenna, cosmology was closely connected to angelology.[22] The Universe was peopled by angelic forces, a view which accorded perfectly well with the religious conception of the world. The spiritual agent in the form of the angel was an integral and real aspect of cosmic reality. As it spread in the West, however, Avicennian cosmology, although accepted in outline, was criticized by men like William of Auvergne who wanted to banish the angels from the Universe. By neglecting the Avicennian souls of the spheres, these scholars had to a certain extent already secularized the Universe and prepared it for the Copernican revolution.[23] This revolution could, in fact, only have occurred in a cosmos from which the symbolic and spiritual meaning had been removed; a cosmos which had become sheer fact drawn away from the bosom of metaphysics and made the subject of a purely physical science.

While the thirteenth century was the golden age of scholasticism and produced the synthesis of St Thomas and a few men like Albertus Magnus, Roger Bacon and Robert Grosseteste who within the matrix of a Christian philosophy were intensely interested in the sciences of nature, the very domination of rationalism during this period soon destroyed the equilibrium established during the century. The balance tilted in the other direction, and in the fourteenth century led to an attack against reason and a scepticism that marked the end of the Middle Ages. Two different but complementary movements can be seen at this time. The first is the destruction of the esoteric organizations within Christendom such as the Order of the Temple. The result was that the gnostic and metaphysical element which had until that time been continuously present began to disperse and gradually disappear, at least as an active living force in the intellectual framework of the Christian West.[24] The second was the foundering of rationalism by its own weight and the introduction of a denial of the power of reason to reach the truth. If the mystics like Meister Eckhart sought to transcend reason from above, the nominalist theologians rejected rational philosophy, one might say from below, by refusing reason the very possibility of knowing the universal.

The whole debate about universals which goes back to Abelard became at this time the favourite weapon for attacking reason and showing the inconsistencies of its conclusions. Ockham and the Ockhamists created an atmosphere of philosophical doubt which they tried to fill with a nominalist theology that was to play the role of philosophy. Ockham created a theologism which destroyed the certainty of medieval philosophy and led to philosophical scepticism.[25] Meanwhile, in emphasizing particular universal causes and criticizing Peripatetic philosophy and science, Ockham and his followers like Oresme and Nicolas of Autrecourt made important discoveries in mechanics and dynamics, discoveries that form the basis of the seventeenth-century revolution in physics. It is important to note, however, that this interest in the sciences of nature went hand in hand with philosophical doubt and a turning away from metaphysics. For this was substituted a nominalist theology. Once the element of faith became weakened this scientific development was left without any element of philosophical certainty. Rather, it became wedded to doubt and scepticism.

The Middle Ages thus drew to a close in a climate in which the symbolic and contemplative view of nature had been for the most part replaced by a rationalistic view, and this in turn through the criticism of nominalist theologians had led to philosophical scepticism. Meanwhile, with the destruction of the gnostic and metaphysical elements within Christianity the cosmological sciences became opaque and incomprehensible and the cosmos itself was gradually secularized. Furthermore, within Christian circles in general, neither the Dominicans nor Franciscans showed particular interest in the study of nature.[26] The background was thus prepared in every way for that revolution and upheaval which brought to an end the integral Christian civilization of the medieval period and created an atmosphere in which the sciences of nature began to be cultivated outside of the world view of Christianity and where the cosmos gradually ceased to be Christian.

With the Renaissance, European man lost the paradise of the age of faith to gain in compensation the new earth of nature and natural forms to which he now turned his attention. Yet it was a nature which came to be less and less a reflection of a celestial reality. Renaissance man ceased to be the ambivalent man of the Middle Ages, half angel, half man, torn between heaven and earth. Rather, he became wholly man, but now a totally earth-bound creature.[27] He gained his liberty at the expense of losing the freedom to transcend his terrestrial limitations. Freedom for him now became quantitative and horizontal rather than qualitative and vertical, and it was in this spirit that he went on to conquer the earth and with it to open new horizons in geography and natural history. However, there still existed a religious significance in wilderness and nature that had come down through the Christian tradition.[28]

This new conception of an earth-bound man which is closely tied to the humanism and anthropomorphism of this period, coincided with the destruction and gradual disappearance of what was left of the initiatic and esoteric organizations of the Middle Ages. The Renaissance was witness to the destruction of such organizations as the Society of the Rosy Cross, while at the same time all kinds of writings associated with secret organizations and societies such as Hermetical and Kabbalistic works began to appear. The vast number of these works during this period is due, however, first and foremost to the destruction of the depositories of this type of knowledge, thus facilitating their profanation and vulgarization. Secondly it is due to an attempt on the part of certain thinkers to discover a primordial religious tradition antedating Christianity so that they turned to all that spoke of the ancient mysteries.[29]

Moreover, when we glance at the sciences of the Renaissance, we see that besides new discoveries in geography and natural history and certain advances in mathematics, the framework is essentially that of the Middle Ages. Renaissance science is continuous with that of the medieval period, despite its accent upon naturalism. This is because what are seen as coming to the fore at this time are the cosmological and occult sciences of the medieval period that are now made to be publicly known and elaborated, albeit sometimes with confusion and distortion. Agrippa, Paracelsus, Basil Valentine, Meier, Bodin and so many other figures belong more to the ancient and medieval tradition of science than to the modern one. Yet the Hermetical and magical schools of the Renaissance have had as significant a role in the creation of modern science as the more frequently studied mathematico-physical school connected with the name of Galileo. Too little attention has been paid to this all important element because of an *a priori* judgement as to what science is.[30]

However, as is to be expected in a period of the eclipse of metaphysical knowledge and even of philosophical doubt, sciences such as alchemy became ever more incomprehensible, opaque and confused until gradually they ceased to be science as such and became the preoccupation of the occultists or the curious. Paracelsus was still at the centre of the scientific stage of his day. By the time Fludd and Kepler were exchanging notes, the Hermetico-alchemical tradition for which Fludd stood had lost the battle, and what was considered as science passed on into the hands of Kepler and his like.

This loss of metaphysical insight and awareness into the symbolic meaning of cosmological sciences is also seen in the rapid transformation of cosmology into cosmography, a movement from content to form. The numerous cosmographies of the Renaissance no longer deal with the content and meaning of the cosmos, but with its form and external description, although they still describe the medieval cosmos.[31] All that is left is the body without its inner spirit and meaning. From these cosmographies to the breakdown of the cosmic picture there is but a single step which comes with the Copernican revolution.

The Copernican revolution brought about all the spiritual and religious upheavals that its opponents forecasted would happen precisely because it came at a time when philosophical doubt reigned everywhere, and a humanism, already over a century old, had taken away from man his position as the 'divine image' on earth. The proposal that the sun is at the centre of the solar system was not in itself new; for it was known by certain Greek, Islamic and Indian philosophers and astronomers. But its proposal during the Renaissance without an accompanying new spiritual vision of things could only mean a dislocation of man in the cosmos.

Theology and the external formulation of religion begins with man and his needs as an immortal being. Metaphysics and the esoteric aspect of tradition deal with the nature of things as such. The Ptolemaic-Aristotelian astronomy corresponds to the more immediately apparent structure of the cosmos and the profound symbolism that the concentric spheres present to man as the visible aspect of the multiple states of being. In this scheme, man is from one point of view at the centre of the Universe by virtue of his theomorphic nature, and from another point of view he is at the lowest level of existence from which he has to ascend toward the divine. The ascent through the cosmos as we see so plainly in the *Divine Comedy* corresponds also to the ascent of the soul through the degrees of purification and of knowledge. By necessity it corresponds to existence itself. Medieval cosmology had therefore, from the spiritual point of view, the advantage of presenting the visible cosmos to men as a concrete symbol of a metaphysical reality which in any case remains true, independently of the symbols used to convey it. Also, by virtue of remaining faithful to the immediate appearance of things as they present themselves to man, the Ptolemaic-Aristotelian astronomy corresponded more to a theological and exoteric truth while at the same time it remained a most powerful symbol of a metaphysical reality.

The heliocentric system also possesses its spiritual symbolism. By placing the source of light at the centre, an argument to which Copernicus himself referred in the introduction of his book *De revolutionibus orbium coelestium*, this astronomy symbolizes clearly the centrality of the Universal Intellect for which the sun, the supernal Apollo, is the most direct symbol. Moreover, by removing the boundaries of the cosmos and presenting to man the vastness of cosmic space, which symbolizes the illimitable vastness of the Divine Being and man's nothingness before this Reality, this view corresponds more to the esoteric perspective based on the total nature of things than to the exoteric and theological that are concerned with man's needs in order that he should be saved. But this astronomy was not accompanied by a new spiritual vision even if occasionally a man like Nicolas of Cusa pointed to the profound significance of the 'infinite universe', 'whose centre is everywhere and whose circumference is nowhere'.[32] The total effect of the new astronomy was like the profanation of an esoteric form of knowledge,[33] somewhat like our observations in the case of the alchemical and Kabbalistic sciences. It presented a new vision of the physical Universe without providing also a spiritual interpretation for it. The transformation from the bound to the 'infinite universe' also had, therefore, the deepest religious repercussions in the souls of men and was closely intertwined with the whole religious and philosophical development of the Renaissance and the seventeenth century.[34]

It may seem at first as if the Copernican revolution moved counter to the prevalent humanism of the time by removing man from the centre of the Universe. This is only an apparent effect;

its deeper effect was to aid the general humanistic and Promethean spirit of the Renaissance. In medieval cosmology man had been placed at the centre of the Universe, not as a purely terrestrial and earth-bound man but as the 'image of God'. His centrality was due not to anthropomorphic qualities but to theomorphic ones. By removing him from the centre of things, the new astronomy did not bestow upon man the transcendent dimension of his nature; rather it affirmed the loss of the theomorphic nature by virtue of which he had been placed at the centre. Therefore, although on the surface it belittled the position of man in the scheme of things, on a deeper level it assisted the tendency toward anthropomorphism and the Promethean revolt against the voice of heaven.

With the destruction of an immutable set of principles which are the judge of both knowledge and virtue, and the appearance of a purely terrestial man who became the measure of all things, a trend from objectivism to subjectivism began in Western civilization which continues to this day. No longer was there a metaphysics and a cosmology to judge the truth and falsehood of what men said, but the thoughts of men in each epoch themselves became the criteria of truth and falsehood. The Renaissance, although still following the formal medieval sciences, brought forth a new conception of man which henceforth made all form of knowledge including science in a certain sense anthropomorphic. It made of 'fallen man's' vision of things, to use the Christian terminology, the truth itself and removed to the greatest possible extent any objective criterion of intellectual knowledge. Henceforth, science was only what the mental could grasp and explain. It could not serve the function of transcending the mental itself through the power of symbolism.

The scientific revolution itself came not in the Renaissance but during the seventeenth century when the cosmos had already become secularized, religion weakened through long, inner conflicts, metaphysics and gnosis in the real sense nearly forgotten and the meaning of symbols neglected, which can be seen in the art of this period. It also came after more than two centuries of philosophical scepticism from which the philosophers of the seventeenth century tried to escape and regain access to certainty. Descartes was the heir to the Christian humanists of the late Middle Ages and the Renaissance, of men like Petrarch, Gehrard Groot and Erasmus as well as the whole group of Renaissance philosophers like Telesio, Campanella and Adriano di Corneto. These latter doubted the power of philosophy to reach certainty about ultimate principles and as compensation usually turned toward ethics and morality. Descartes was also most of all heir to the scepticism expressed in the *Essays* of Montaigne to which his *Discours* is an answer in more than one way.[35]

In order to reach certainty in knowledge through his famous method, Descartes had to reduce the rich diversity of external reality to pure quantity and philosophy to mathematics. His was a mathematicism, to use the term of Gilson,[36] and henceforth Cartesian mathematicism became a permanent element of the scientific world view. The physics Descartes constructed through his method was rejected by Newton. His zoology in which he sought to reduce animals to machines was violently attacked and refuted by Henry More and John Ray. But his mathematicism, the attempt to reduce reality to pure quantity with which one could then deal in a purely mathematical way, has become the background of mathematical physics and unconsciously of many other sciences which desperately seek to find quantitative relationships between things by overlooking their qualitative aspect. The distinction made by Galileo in the *Discorsi* between primary and secondary qualities is an affirmation of Descartes' reduction of reality to quantity, although Galileo succeeded in creating a new physics where Descartes failed.

The genius of Newton was able to create a synthesis from the works of Descartes, Galileo and Kepler and to present a picture of the world which Newton, himself a religious man, felt was a confirmation of a spiritual order in the Universe. In fact the background of Newton's thought, connected with such figures as Isaac Burrows and the Cambridge Platonists, was far from being divorced from interest in the metaphysical meaning of time, space and motion. Yet the Newtonian world view led to the well-known mechanistic conception of the Universe and totally away from the holistic and organic interpretation of things. The result was that after the seventeenth century science and religion became totally divorced. Newton was one of the first to realize the adverse theological effects of his discoveries. We must not forget how much effort he spent and how many pages he wrote on the alchemical and Kabbalistic sciences of his day. Perhaps for him the new physics, with its eminent success on the mathematico-physical level, was just a science of material things. For those who followed him it became *the* science, the only legitimate knowledge of the objective world.

Also in the seventeenth century the last step in the secularization of the cosmos took place in the hands of the philosophers and scientists. In the Renaissance elements of traditional philosophy still survived. The anatomy of existence consisted not only of the physical and the purely intelligible worlds but also of the intermediary world between matter and pure spirit, the 'imaginal world' (*mundus imaginalis*). This, however, must not be considered in any way unreal or made to correspond to the modern meaning of 'imaginary'. Such an intermediate world was the immediate principle of nature, and through it the symbolic science of nature was made possible. Among Christian thinkers (albeit away from the centre of theological orthodoxy), even after the Renaissance a man like Swedenborg could write a hermeneutic commentary upon the Bible which was also an exposition of a symbolic science of nature and could rely upon this intermediate world as the meeting ground of spiritual and material forms.[37] The Cambridge Platonists, particularly Henry More, were, however, the last of the European philosophers to speak of this domain of reality in the same way that Leibniz was the last major Western philosopher to speak of the angels.

Henceforth the Cartesian surgical operation in which spirit and matter become totally separated dominated scientific and philosophic thought. The domain of science was matter which was a pure 'it' divorced completely from any ontological aspect other than pure quantity. Although there were protests here and there especially among English and German thinkers, this view became the very factor that determined the relationship between man and nature, scientifically and philosophically. Thus seventeenth-century rationalism is the unconscious background of all later scientific thought up to the present day. Whatever discoveries are made in the sciences and whatever changes are brought about in conceptions of time, space, matter and motion, the background of seventeenth-century rationalism remains. For this very reason, other interpretations of nature, especially the symbolic, have never been seriously considered and accepted.

In the seventeenth century Hermeticism still continued strongly particularly in England. There was also Jacob Böhme, the re-markable cobbler and theosopher in Germany, whose very appearance at this time is most significant and who influenced deeply the school of *Naturphilosophie* that reacted so severely against the prevalent mechanical philosophy. These develop-ments are of importance as showing the continuity in certain circles, especially of northern Europe, of a spiritual conception of nature. These schools still remained peripheral as far as their influence on modern science was concerned. The centre of the stage continued to be occupied by mechanistic philosophy and science.

During the eighteenth century, while theoretically science continued along lines established in the seventeenth, its philo-sophic effect was more pronounced. The philosophy of Descartes was drawn to its logical conclusion by the Empiricists, by Hume and by Kant who demonstrated the inability of purely human reason to reach knowledge of the essence of things, thereby opening the door to the irrational philosophies that have followed since his advent. Through the 'encyclopedists', Rousseau and Voltaire, a philosophy of man without a transcendent dimension became popularized and truth reduced to utility.[38] If the seven-teenth century still considered problems on the level of their theoretical truth or falsehood, the question now became the utility of knowledge for man, who had now become nothing but a creature of the earth with no other end but to exploit and dominate its riches. This practical and utilitarian bent, crystallized by the French Revolution, accentuated the effect of the new mechanistic science by turning more attention to the empirical sciences and seeking to destroy any vestiges of a contemplative view toward nature that still survived.[39] With the help of the new science the only role left to man was to conquer and dominate nature and to serve his needs as an animal endowed somehow with analytical reason and thought.

The materialistic conception of nature did not go unchallenged during the nineteenth century, particularly in art and literature where the romantic movement sought to re-establish a more intimate bond with nature and the indwelling spirit within nature. The philosophical Romantic poets like Novalis devoted themselves most of all to the theme of nature and its significance for man. One of the foremost among them, Wordsworth, could write in the *Excursion* (Book IX):

> 'To every Form of being is assigned'
> Thus calmly spake the venerable Sage,
> 'An *active* Principle:—howe'er removed
> From sense and observation, it subsists
> In all things, in all natures; in the stars
> Of azure heaven, the unenduring clouds,
> In flower and tree, in every pebbly stone
> That paves the brooks, the stationary rocks,
> The morning waters, and the invisible air.
> Whate'er exists hath properties that spread
> Beyond itself, communicating good,
> A simple blessing, or with evil mixed;
> Spirit that knows no insulated spot,
> No chasm, no solitude; from link to link
> It circulates, the soul of all the worlds.
> This is the freedom of the universe;'

Likewise a man like John Ruskin saw nature as something

divine[40] and spoke of the 'spiritual power of air, the rocks, and waters'.[41]

The romantic attitude toward nature, however, was more sentimental than intellectual. Wordsworth speaks of 'wise passiveness' and Keats of 'negative capability'. This passive attitude could not make and mould knowledge. Whatever service the romantic movement rendered in re-discovering medieval art or the beauty of virgin nature, it could not affect the current of science nor add a new dimension within science itself by which man would be able to understand those aspects of nature that seventeenth century science and its aftermath had failed to consider.

As for the philosophy of the nineteenth century it surrendered the possibility of knowing things in their immutable aspect and so became, with Hegel, bound to process and change. The Absolute itself was made to enter the current of the dialectical process which was equated with a new logic of process and becoming. The vision of a changeless and immutable reality became completely forgotten in a universe where, for some time now, suprasensible reality had lost its objective and ontological status. The intuitions of men like Schelling or Franz von Baader could do little to turn the tide away from a further plunge into the world of sheer becoming and change.

As for science, the major event occurred in biology where the theory of evolution reflects more the '*zeitgeist*' than a scientific theory. In a world where the 'multiple states of being' had lost their meaning, where the archetypal reality of species held no significance, where there was no metaphysical and philosophical background to enable men to interpret the appearance of different species on earth as so many successive 'dreams of the World Soul', where the hands of the Creator had been cut off from creation through the spread of Deism there could be no other explanation for the multiplicity of the species than temporal evolution. The vertical 'chain of being' had to be made temporal and horizontal,[42] whatever absurdities such a view might imply metaphysically and theologically. The result of this theory, besides causing endless bickerings between popularizers of evolution and theologians, brought a further alienation of man from nature by removing from the world of life the immutable form or essence of things which alone can be intellectually contemplated and can become the object of metaphysical knowledge and vision. It also condoned all kinds of excesses in usurping the right of other forms of life in the name of the 'survival of the fittest'.

The theory of evolution did not provide an organic view for the physical sciences but provided men with a way of reducing the higher to the lower, a magical formula to apply everywhere in order to explain things without the need to have recourse to any higher principles or causes. It also went hand in hand with a prevalent historicism which is a parody of the Christian philosophy of history, but which nevertheless could only take place in the Christian world where the truth itself had become incarnated in time and history. A reaction is always against an existing affirmation and action.

With the breakdown of classical physics at the end of the nineteenth century, there was no spiritual force ready to reinterpret the new science and integrate it into a more universal perspective. Some found in this breakdown a chance to re-assert other points of view which the monolithic mechanistic conception of the Universe had previously prevented. Also, the breakdown meant on the one hand a re-interpretation of science which destroyed even further contact with the macrocosmic world and the immediate symbolism of things. (This can be seen in the case of the change from Euclidian geometry to those of Riemann or Lobachevski.) On the other hand it meant the opening of the gate to all kinds of pseudo-spiritual movements and occult sciences which graft themselves upon the newest theories of physics, but which are usually either degenerate residues of older cosmological sciences, now no longer understood, or simply dangerous and pernicious inventions. From the genuinely religious quarters the breakdown of classical physics did not bring forth a vigorous response that could lead to a meaningful

— complementary sciences —

synthesis. For the most part the theological response has been a
weak echo that has often adopted discarded ideas of science
itself and sometimes, as in the case of Teilhard de Chardin, has
sought a synthesis which is metaphysically an absurdity and
theologically a heresy.[43]

It is this long history, some of whose features have been pointed
out here, that has at last led to the present crisis in the encounter
between man and nature. As pointed out in Chapter I it is only
through a re-discovery of true metaphysics, especially the
sapiential doctrines of Christianity and the revival of that tradition
within Christianity which has done justice to the relation between man and nature, that a hierarchy of knowledge can be
again asserted and a symbolic science of nature re-established
which will effectively complement the quantitative sciences of
today. Only in this way can an equilibrium be created, an equilibrium from which the development of the past few centuries has
drawn away with ever greater speed until today the disequilibrium and lack of harmony between man and nature threatens to
destroy them both together. Thus we must turn to a discussion of
metaphysics and the tradition of the spiritual study of nature
within Christianity.

NOTES TO CHAPTER II

1. 'Historians of science have, until recently, committed the same error as
historians of the early Church in the fourth and fifth centuries; they have
written as if the only events of importance in the previous period were those
which directly anticipated and promoted the current orthodoxy of their own
day.' Raven, *Natural Religion and Christian Theology*, I, p. 7.

2. Whereas science in English should logically mean the *scientia* of Latin
or *Wissenschaft* of German it has come to acquire a very restricted meaning
in most quarters leaving the English language without a general term corresponding to *Wissenschaft*, or *scientia*. Recently in certain circles the full
meaning of 'science' has been re-instated but this more universal meaning is
far from being widely accepted or employed.

3. Fortunately, in the past few years, some historians of science have turned their attention to the study of ancient and medieval science as related to the total world view of the cultures of these ages rather than as simply historical preludes to modern science. Due to the lack of metaphysical knowledge and disregard for the science of symbolism, this approach has not been wide-spread.

4. One hardly need re-assert how many modern scholars insist on the close nexus between science and Christian thought. Some take into consideration positive relations and others the reactions between the two. See for example, Smethurst, *Modern Science and Christian Belief*, J. MacMurray, *Reason and Emotion*, London, 1935; J. Baillie, *Natural Science and the Spiritual Life*, London, 1951; and S. F. Mason, *Main Currents of Scientific Thought*, New York, 1956.

5. See F. Cornford, *Principium sapientiae*, Cambridge, 1952; and W. Jaeger, *Theology of the Early Greek Philosophers*, Oxford, 1947.

6. See Cornford, *From Religion to Philosophy*, New York, 1958, Also G. DiSantillana, *Foundations of Scientific Thought*, Chicago, 1961.

7. See F. Schuon, *Light on the Ancient Worlds*, p. 64.

8. Of course Stoicism has had much importance during the Renaissance and the seventeenth century as a weapon against Aristotelianism and has contributed much to the rise of seventeenth-century physics as shown by S. Sambursky in *Physics of the Stoics*, New York, 1959. But nevertheless it cannot be denied that the scientific achievements of the Stoics, Epicureans and similar late schools that were disseminated in the Roman Empire hardly compare with that of Aristotle or the school of Alexandria in general.

It is also of interest to note that after Aristotle himself his school turned mostly from a study of the organic aspect of nature, as witnessed in the biological works of Aristotle and the botany of Theophrastus, to an interest in mechanics and simple machines as seen in the pseudo-Aristotelian *Mechanics*.

9. See B. Bavink, 'The Natural Sciences' in, *Introduction to the Scientific Philosophy of Today*, New York, 1932, where the author writes that except for a few Teutons, St Francis of Assisi, the German mystics and Luther, Christianity has neglected the study of nature outside of the human being. See particularly p. 576.

10. Referring to the debate and dialogue between the Christian and the Hellenist Schuon writes, '. . . a half truth which tends to safeguard the transcendence of God at the expense of the metaphysical intelligibility of the world is less erroneous than a half-truth which tends to safeguard the divine nature of the world at the expense of the intelligibility of God.' *Light on the Ancient Worlds*, p. 60.

On the struggle between early Christian theology and the 'cosmic religion' of the Greeks see J. Pépin, *Théologie cosmique et théologie chrétienne*, Paris, 1964. *p93*

11. By gnosis of course we mean that unitive knowledge which saves and illumines and is inseparable from love and not gnosticism which was banned as a heresy by the Christian councils.

12. On this question see T. Burckhardt, 'Nature de la perspective cosmologique', *Etudes Traditionnelles*, vol. 49, 1948, pp. 216–19; and in the context of Islam, S. H. Nasr, *An Introduction to Islamic Cosmological Doctrines*, Cambridge (U.S.A.), 1964, especially the introduction.

13. Traditional cosmology is very much like sacred art which, out of the many forms of the world of multiplicity, chooses a certain number which it moulds and transmutes so as to make of them an intelligible and transparent symbol of the spiritual genius of the religious tradition in question. See Burckhardt, 'Nature de la perspective cosmologique'.

14. See 'Aesthetics and Symbolism in Art and Nature' in F. Schuon, *Spiritual Perspectives and Human Facts*, pp. 24 ff.

15. It is not accidental that the walls of European cities began to be broken about the same time that heliocentric astronomy destroyed the idea of the world as cosmos or 'order' and removed the finite boundary of the Universe.

16. See the Appendix of E. Levy in O. von Simpson, *The Gothic Cathedral*, New York, 1956; also T. Burckhardt, *Chartres und die Geburt der Kathedrale*, Lausanne and Freiburg, 1962. H. Keyser in many studies such as *Akroasis, die Lehre von Harmonike der Welt*, Stuttgart, 1947, has re-discovered for the modern world this forgotten traditional science of harmony which is so important as an integrating principle of the arts and the sciences. The *trivium* and *quadrivium*, the medieval arts and sciences themselves, come from the Pythagorean seven-fold division of the musical scale.

17. See M. Aniane, 'Notes sur l'alchimie, "yoga" cosmologique de la chrétienté médiévale', in *Yoga, science de l'homme intégral*, Paris, 1953, pp. 243–73; also T. Burckhardt, *Die Alchemie, Sinn und Weltbild*, Osten, 1960; and S. H. Nasr, 'The Alchemical Tradition' in *Science and Civilization in Islam*, Cambridge (U.S.A.), 1968.

18. See H. Probst-Biraben, *Les Mystères des templiers*, Nice, 1947; also P. Ponsoye, *Islam et le Graal*, Paris, 1957.

19. As far as the relation between the sciences, philosophy and the gnostic and Sufi dimension within Islam is concerned see S. H. Nasr, *Three Muslim Sages*, Cambridge (U.S.A.), 1964; *An Introduction to Islamic Cosmological Doctrines* and *Science and Civilization in Islam*.

20. See *Three Muslim Sages*, Chapter I.

21. See, *An Introduction to Islamic Cosmological Doctrines*, pp. 185–91.

22. See H. Corbin, *Avicenna and the Visionary Recital*, section II; also S. H. Nasr, *Three Muslim Sages*, pp. 28–31.

23. Corbin, *op. cit.*, pp. 101 ff.

24. See R. Guénon, *Aperçu sur l'ésotérisme chrétien*, Paris, 1954.

25. E. Gilson, *The Unity of Philosophical Experience*, London, 1938, pp. 62 ff.

26. 'That neither Fransiscans nor Dominicans succeeded in establishing a serious regard for the study of nature within the Church, during the century in which medieval Christendom rose to its splendid zenith, made inevitable the upheavals and revolts of the Renaissance and Reformation.' Raven, *Science and Religion*, p. 72.

27. See F. Schuon, *Light on the Ancient Worlds*, Chapter II, 'In the Wake of the Fall'.

28. See G. Williams, *Wilderness and Paradise in Christian Thought*, Chapter III.

29. For the analysis of this aspect of the question as far as Hermeticism is concerned see M. Eliade, 'The Quest for the "Origin" of Religion', *History of Religions*, vol. IV, no. 1, Summer 1964, pp. 156 ff.

30. Only a small number of scholars such as W. Pagel and in recent years A. Debus and F. Yates have studied and made known the immense influence of the Paracelsian and alchemical tradition of the Renaissance in seventeenth-century sciences.

31. See T. Burckhardt 'Cosmology and Modern Science', pp. 183–4.

32. Already a century before Copernicus Nicolas of Cusa in his *De docta ignorantia* referred to the earth as a star and believed in an unbounded Universe to whose metaphysical and esoteric significance he pointed more than once. See R. Klibansky, 'Copernic et Nicolas de Cuse', in *Léonard de Vinci et l'expérience scientifique du XVIe siècle*, Paris, 1953.

33. 'The heliocentric system itself admits of an obvious symbolism, since it identifies the source of light with the centre of the world. Its rediscovery by Copernicus, however, produced no new spiritual vision of the world; rather was it comparable to the dangerous popularization of an esoteric truth. The heliocentric system has no common measure with the subjective experiences of the people, in it man had no organic place; instead of helping the human mind to go beyond itself and to consider things in terms of the immensity of the cosmos, it only encouraged a materialistic Prometheanism

which, far from being superhuman, ended by becoming inhuman.' Burckhardt, 'Cosmology and Modern Science', pp. 184–5.

34. See A. Koyré, *From the Closed World to the Infinite Universe*, New York, 1958.

35. See E. Gilson, *The Unity of Philosophical Experience*, p. 127.

36. Gilson, *ibid.*, Chapter V.

37. See H. Corbin, *Herméneutique spirituelle comparée* (*I. Swedenborg-II. Gnose ismaélienne*), *Eranos Jahrbuch*, Zürich, 1965.

38. 'With Voltaire, Rousseau and Kant bourgeois unintelligence erects itself into a "doctrine" and becomes definitely entrenched in European "thought", giving birth, through the French Revolution, to positivist science, industry and quantitative "culture". Henceforward the mental hypertrophy of the "cultured" man ekes out the absence of intellectual penetration; all feeling for the absolute and for principles is drowned in a commonplace empiricism, on to which is grafted a pseudo-mysticism with "positivistic" or "humanistic" tendencies. Perhaps some people will reproach us with lack of reticence, but we would like to ask where is the reticence of the philosophers who shamelessly slash at the wisdom of countless centuries.' F. Schuon, *Language of the Self* (trans. M. Pallis and D. M. Matheson), Madras, 1959, p. 8, nt. 1.

39. 'At the time of the Revolution of the late eighteenth century, the earth had become definitely and exclusively the goal of man; the "Supreme Being" was merely a "consolation" and as such a target for ridicule; the seemingly infinite multitude of things on earth called for an infinity of activities, which furnished a pretext for rejecting contemplation . . ., man was at last free to busy himself, on the hither side of transcendence, with the discovery of the terrestrial world and the exploitation of its riches; he was at last rid of symbols, rid of metaphysical transparence; there was no longer anything but the agreeable or the disagreeable, the useful or the useless, whence the anarchic and irresponsible development of the experimental sciences.' Schuon, *Light on the Ancient Worlds*, p. 30.

40. 'Ruskin looked at the material universe with preternatural vivacity and clarity, and believed that what he saw was divine.' J. Rosenberg, *The Darkening Glass, a Portrait of Ruskin's Genius*, New York, 1961, pp. 4–5.

41. *Ibid.*, p. 7.

42. On the chain of being and its relation to the theory of evolution see, O. Lovejoy, *The Great Chains of Being*, Cambridge, (U.S.A.), 1933.

43. 'As a symptom of our time, Teilhardism, is comparable to one of those cracks that are due to the very solidification of the mental carapace, and

which do not open upwards, towards the heaven of true and transcendent unity, but downward towards the realm of the inferior psychism: weary of its own discontinuous vision of the world, the materialist mind lets itself slide toward a pseudo-spiritual intoxication, of which this falsified and materialized faith—or this sublimated materialism—that we have just described marks a phase of particular significance.' Burckhardt, 'Cosmology and Modern Science', *Tomorrow*, Autumn, 1964, p. 315.

Chapter 3

Some Metaphysical Principles Pertaining to Nature

We have so far often mentioned metaphysics. It is now time to define what we mean by this all important form of knowledge, whose disappearance is most directly responsible for our modern predicament. Metaphysics, which in fact is one and should be named metaphysic in the singular, is the science of the Real, of the origin and end of things, of the Absolute and, in its light, the relative. It is a science as strict and exact as mathematics and with the same clarity and certitude, but one which can only be attained through intellectual intuition and not simply through ratiocination. It thus differs from philosophy as it is usually understood.[1] Rather, it is a *theoria* of reality whose realization means sanctity and spiritual perfection, and therefore can only be achieved within the cadre of a revealed tradition. Metaphysical intuition can occur anywhere—for the 'spirit bloweth where it listeth'—but the effective realization of metaphysical truth and its application to human life can only be achieved within a revealed tradition which gives efficacy to certain symbols and rites upon which metaphysics must rely for its realization.

This supreme science of the Real, which in a certain light is the same as gnosis, is the only science that can distinguish between the Absolute and the relative, appearance and reality. It is only in its light that man can distinguish between levels of reality and states of being and be able to see each thing in its place in the total scheme of things. Moreover, this science exists, as the esoteric dimension, within every orthodox and integral tradition and is

81

united with a spiritual method derived totally from the sources of the tradition in question.

In the traditions of the East, metaphysics has been continuously alive to this day, and despite differences of foundation there is a unity of doctrine which justifies the use of the term 'Oriental Metaphysics',[2] although metaphysics knows no Orient or Occident. In the West there has also been true metaphysics of the highest order, among the Greeks in the Pythagorean-Platonic writings, and especially in Plotinus. In all these cases metaphysics is the doctrinal exposition that was the fruit of a living spiritual way. Likewise in Christianity one finds metaphysics in the writings of some of the early founders of Christian theology like Clement and Origen, Irenaeus, Gregory of Nyssa and Gregory of Nazianzen, in Erigena, Dante and Eckhart and again in Jacob Böhme. Among Orthodox writers there is an even more open and complete metaphysical exposition than that which is found among Latin authors. But even the official theology of the Latin church, especially the Augustinian school, contains metaphysics which, however, is much more hidden and indirect.

In Western philosophy, however, since Aristotle the unfortunate practice of considering metaphysics as a branch of philosophy came into being so that with the appearance of philosophical doubt metaphysics has also been discredited. In this domain, the rationalism of later Greek philosophy fortified the tendency within official Christian theology to emphasize will and love rather than intelligence and sapiential knowledge. These two factors combined to make of metaphysics and gnosis a peripheral aspect of the intellectual life of Western man, especially since the end of the Middle Ages and the Renaissance. What is usually called metaphysics in post-medieval philosophy is, for the most part, nothing but an extension of rationalistic philosophy and at best a pale reflection of true metaphysics. The so-called metaphysics that philosophers like Heidegger have criticized and consider as having come to an end is not the metaphysical doctrine we have in mind. Metaphysics, tied to a philosophy that is at once perennial and universal, knows no beginning or end.

It is the heart of the *philosophia perennis* to which Leibnitz referred.

In as much as the loss of metaphysical knowledge is responsible for the loss of harmony between man and nature and of the role of the sciences of nature in the total scheme of knowledge, and by the fact that this knowledge has been nearly forgotten in the West while it has continued to survive in the traditions of the East, it is to these Oriental traditions that one must turn in order to rediscover the metaphysical significance of nature and to revive the metaphysical tradition within Christianity. If the East is learning by compulsion and necessity the Western techniques of domination over nature, it is from Oriental metaphysics that one must learn how to prevent this domination from becoming sheer self-annihilation.

Turning first to the Far East we see in the Chinese tradition, especially in Taoism and also in Neo-Confucianism, a devotion to nature and a comprehension of its metaphysical significance that is of the greatest importance. This same reverential attitude toward nature, together with a strong sense of symbolism and an awareness of the lucidity of the cosmos and its transparency before metaphysical realities, is to be found in Japan. Shintoism has strongly fortified this attitude. That is why in the art of the Far East, especially in the Taoist and Zen traditions, paintings of natural scenes are veritable icons. They do not just evoke a sentimental pleasure in the onlooker but convey grace, and are a means of communion with transcendental reality.

In Taoism there is always the awareness of the presence of the transcendent dimension symbolized by the void so dominant in landscape paintings. But this void is not non-being in the negative sense, but the Non-Being which transcends even Being and is dark only because of an excess of light. It is like the divine darkness to which Dionysius the Areopagite refers, or the wilderness of Godhead (*die wüsste Gottheit*) of Meister Eckhart. That is why this Non-Being or Void is also the principle of Being, and through Being the principle of all things. So we read in the sacred text of Taoism, the *Tao Te-Ching*:

83

'All things under Heaven are products of Being, but Being itself is the product of Not-Being.'[3] In this simple assertion is contained the principle of all metaphysics, in pointing to the hierarchic structure of reality and the dependence of all that is relative upon the Absolute and the Infinite, symbolized by the Void or Non-Being that is unbound and limitless. Likewise Chuang-Tzu affirms the same principle somewhat more elaborately when he writes:

'In the Grand Beginning (of all things) there was nothing in all the vacancy of space; there was nothing that could be named. It was in this state that there arose the first existence;—the first existence, but still without bodily shape. From this things could then be produced (receiving) what we call their proper character. That which had no bodily shape was divided; and then without intermission there was what we call the process of conferring. (The two processes) continuing in operation, things were produced. As things were completed, there were produced the distinguishing lines of each, which we call the bodily shape. That shape was the body preserving in it the spirit, and each had its peculiar manifestations, which we call its Nature. When the Nature has been cultivated, it returns to its proper character; and when that has been fully reached, there is the same condition as at the beginning.'[4]

In as much as Heaven, in the metaphysical sense, and in its characteristic Chinese usage, comes from the Origin and Earth, again in its metaphysical significance, from Heaven, man must live in this world with a full awareness of the hierarchy. For as the *Tao-Te Ching* asserts: 'The ways of men are conditioned by those of earth, the ways of earth by those of heaven, the ways of heaven by those of the Tao, and the Tao comes into being by itself.'[5] Heaven is thus a reflection of the Supreme Principle and the Earth the reflection of heaven. The Earth of Taoism is not profane nature that stands as gravity opposed to grace, but it is an image of a divine prototype whose contemplation leads upward toward that reality for which 'heaven' is the traditional expression. For this reason also the world can be known, in a metaphysical and not empirical sense, through its Cause and Principle.

'The World has a First Cause, which may be regarded as the Mother of the World. When one has found the Mother, one can know the Child. Knowing the Child and still keeping the Mother, to the end of his days he shall suffer no harm.'[6]

That science is safe and without harm which realizes the manifestation without losing sight of the Principle.

It is of cardinal importance that the Tao is both the Principle, the way to attain the Principle and also the order of things. It is in fact the order of nature[7] if we remember all that Taoism means by nature. Tao, the Principle that is also the order and harmony of all things, is everywhere present, in everything that is great or small. 'The Tao does not exhaust itself in what is greatest, nor is it ever absent from what is least; and therefore it is to be found complete and diffused in all things.'[8] To live in peace and harmony with nature or the Earth, one must live in harmony with Heaven, and in order to attain this end one must live according to the Tao and in conformity with it, the Tao which pervades all things and also transcends all things.[9]

Nature, as the direct effect of the Tao and its laws, stands as opposed to the trivialities of human artefacts and the artificiality with which man surrounds himself. For as Chuang-Tzu says, 'what is of Nature is internal. What is of man is external ... That oxen and horses should have four feet is what is of Nature. That a halter should be put on a horse's head, or a string through an ox's nose, is what is of man.'[10] That is why the aim of the spiritual man is to contemplate nature and become one with it, to become 'natural'. This is not intended in a pantheistic or naturalistic sense, but in a metaphysical sense, so that to become natural means to abide fully by the Tao which is at once both transcendent and the principle of nature. The aim of the sage is to be in harmony with nature for through this harmony comes harmony with men and this harmony is itself the reflection of harmony with heaven. Chuang Tzu writes, 'Anyone who sees clearly the

excellence of all nature may be called God's Trunk or God's
Stock, because he is in harmony with nature. Anyone who brings
the world into accord is in harmony with his fellow men and
happy with men. Whoever is in harmony with nature is happy
with nature.'[11]

To be happy with nature means precisely to accept its norms
and its rhythms rather than to seek to dominate and overcome it.
Nature should not be judged according to human utility nor
earthly man made the measure of all things. There is no anthropomorphism connected with man's relation with nature.[12] Man
should accept and follow the nature of things and not seek to
disturb nature by artificial means.[13] Perfect action is to act without
acting, without self-interest and attachment, or, in other words,
according to nature which acts freely and without greed, lust or
other ulterior motives. There is in fact in Taoism an opposition
to the application of the sciences of nature for the purely material
welfare of man as seen in the well-known story recorded in the
works of Chuang-Tzu:

'Hwang-Tî had been on the throne for nineteen years, and his
ordinances were in operation all through the kingdom, when he
heard that Kwang Khăng-Tze [a Taoist sage] was living on the
summit of Khung-Thung, and went to see him. "I have heard,"
he said, "that you, Sir, are well acquainted with the perfect Tâo.
I venture to ask you what is the essential thing in it. I wish to
take the subtlest influences of heaven and earth, and assist with
them the (growth of the) five cereals for the (better) nourishment
of the people. I also wish to direct the (operation of the) Yin and
Yang, so as to secure the comfort of all living beings. How shall
I proceed to accomplish those objects?" Kwang Khăng-Tze re-
plied, "What you wish to ask about is the original substance of
all things; what you wish to have the direction of is that substance
as it was shattered and divided. According to your government
of the world, the vapours of the clouds, before they were collected, would descend in rain; the herbs and trees would shed
their leaves before they become yellow; and the light of the sun
and moon would hasten to extinction. Your mind is that of a

flatterer with his plausible words;—it is not fit that I should tell you the perfect Tâo.'"[14]

It must be remembered that this same Chinese civilization in which such a contemplative view of nature was cultivated, and where there was even opposition to the application of the sciences of nature, developed physics, mathematics, astronomy and natural history and furthermore has been known throughout history for its technological prowess and genius. It must, moreover, be remembered that most of the early alchemists, geologists and pharmacologists in China were Taoists;[15] and that the polarization of Heaven and Earth and the religious significance of nature persisted as long as the Chinese tradition remained strong. The metaphysical significance of nature as expounded in Taoism, and also Buddhism, while even contributing to the development of sciences of nature, remained as a balance which preserved the hierarchy of knowledge and prevented nature from becoming profane.

The Chinese even developed an astronomical system, the *Hsüan yeh*, which like post-Copernican astronomy was based on an unlimited conception of space and time and was even used by proponents of the Copernican system in Europe against Ptolemaic astronomy. But in China this 'open cosmos' was again wedded to a metaphysical explanation and never allowed to destroy the harmony between man and nature that is so central to the Far Eastern traditions.

In Japan, likewise, we find the Taoist and also Buddhist conceptions of nature coming from China integrated with the local Shinto religion in which again, like all branches of the Shamanic tradition, there is a particular emphasis upon the significance of nature in a cultic sense.[16] Among a people with remarkable artistic sensitivity there developed the most intimate contact with nature, from rock gardens and landscape paintings to flower arrangements, all based on the knowledge of cosmic correspondences, sacred geography, the symbolism of directions, forms and colours. Spiritual methods became closely allied to the inward contemplation of nature and intimacy with its rhythms and forms.

The avid quest after things Japanese in the West in recent years is in many cases the sign of a hidden nostalgia to find peace with nature again and to escape the ugliness of the ambiance created by modern technology. In their special devotion to nature as a means of grace and spiritual sustenance, the traditions of the Far East in their metaphysics, science and art have a cardinal message for the modern world in which the encounter of man and nature is almost always on the basis of war and rarely of the peace which is so avidly sought after and so rarely found.

When we turn to the Hindu tradition, there also we find an elaborate metaphysical doctrine concerning nature along with the development of many sciences in the bosom of Hinduism, some of which in fact influenced Western science through Islam. When we think about the Hindu tradition, our attention usually turns to the Vedantic doctrine of *Atman* and *māya*, the world being considered not as absolute reality but as a veil that hides the Supreme Self. A simplistic interpretation of such a view, especially as prevalent among modern pseudo-Vedantins, would conclude that the world being *māya*, usually translated as illusion, it matters little whether one lives in virgin nature or the ugliest urban environment, whether one surrounds oneself with sacred art or the worst trash produced by the machine.

But this view is itself the worst possible delusion. It is *māya* pure and simple. What Hinduism asserts, like all Oriental doctrines, is the need to gain deliverance from the cosmos which is *māya*. But *māya* is not only illusion, which is its negative aspect, but also the divine play or art.[17] It veils the Supreme Self, the Absolute Reality, but also reveals and displays it. From the point of view of *Atman* or *Brahman*, the Universe is unreal; only the Absolute itself is Real in the absolute sense. For one living in *māya* the relative reality in which he finds himself is at least as real as his own empirical self, and can moreover, be an aid in his gaining deliverance. Although the cosmos is a prison for the sage it is also possible to transcend this prison through a knowledge of its structure and even with its aid. That is why Hinduism as an integral tradition has developed elaborate cosmological and natural sciences and even spiritual techniques tied intimately to the use of the energy within nature. Yet, every science, physical, mathematical and alchemical, as well as the properly religious and spiritual ones, are connected to the total matrix both of Hinduism and in certain cases Buddhism and to the metaphysical principles dominating the whole tradition.[18]

Among the six *darshānas* or intellectual schools of Hinduism, none is as analytical and attached to the corporeal world as the *Vaiśeṣika*. This school is concerned with the physical world and holds a thoroughly atomistic view, beginning with the five elements or *bhutas* from which bodies are formed. It seems on the surface a system most akin to the atomistic and mechanistic physics that developed in the West in late Antiquity and again in the seventeenth century and which was usually anti-religious in its sentiment.[19] But in Hinduism, as in Buddhism, there developed an atomism combined with a spiritual view of the Universe. The *Vaiśeṣika* system is based on the knowledge of the six categories or *padārthas* which are: substance, attribute or quality, action, generality, individuality and inherence. Substance itself is nine kinds: earth, water, fire, air, ether, time, space, mind and spirit. Knowledge of the physical world, or ultimately these six categories, is correct knowledge (*tattvajñāpna*), a knowledge that can only be attained through inner purity and with the help of *dharma* or grace, for it must be remembered that in the *Nyāya-Vaiśeṣika* system above the six *padārthas* stands Iśvara, the Personal Deity, who is the cause of the world.

A system as analytic and as closely concerned with natural things as the *Vaiśeṣika*, has as its end the deliverance of the soul from the atomistic world to which it is attracted by false knowledge.[20] In fact at the beginning of one of the main treatises of this school, the *Padārthadharmasangraha*, it is said, 'A treatise that deals with the properties of things can never lead to the highest bliss; as words cannot accomplish anything besides the denoting of the vernal meanings'. To which objection the answer is given; 'A knowledge of the true nature of the six categories—

substance, quality, action, generality, individuality and inherence—through their similarities and dissimilarities—is the
means of accomplishing the highest bliss'.[21]

Knowledge of the external world is ultimately knowledge of
oneself and even an analytical cosmological and natural science
is not divorced from man's entelechy in the highest sense, namely
deliverance from all limitation. This is not anthropomorphism at
all. On the contrary it is the only form of knowledge through
which man can escape the limitations of his own ego. Concerning
the traditional founder of the *Vaiśeṣika* system, Kaṇāda, it has
been said; 'He [Kaṇāda] had accomplished the knowledge of the
principles (*tattvas*), dispassion and lordliness. He thought within
himself that the knowledge of the principles of the six *padārthas*
(predicables), by means of their resemblances and differences, is
the only royal road to the attainment of self-realization, and that
that would be easily accomplished by the disciples through the
dharma (merit or worth) of renunciation.'[22] Thus the knowledge
of nature is inextricably bound to moral and spiritual laws and
the purity of the seeker after this knowledge. It seems as if
Hinduism like so many other traditions had felt intuitively that
the only safe way to penetrate the mysteries of nature and to
cultivate physics, in the universal sense of this term, is to become
saintly and to seek the saintly life.

Another of the *darśānas*, the *Sāṃkhya*, which contains one
of the most elaborate cosmologies and natural philosophies in
any tradition, likewise begins with the problem of the threefold pain present in the soul and the means to remove this pain,
as is clearly asserted at the beginning of the *Sāṃkhya Kārikā*.[23]
The three kinds of pain, which are the natural and intrinsic such
as diseases, the natural and extrinsic such as any pain caused by
an external source and finally divine or supernatural pain caused
by spiritual factors, can only be overcome by an analytical
knowledge of the three principles of this school, namely, the
prime substance or nature (*Prakriti*), manifested matter that is
in a state of flux (*vyakti*) and finally the Spirit that neither begets
nor is begotten (*Puruṣa*).

The *Sāmkhya* system seeks to remove the pain and misery of the soul through discriminative knowledge, *Sāmkhya* itself meaning etymologically discrimination.[24] It begins with *Prakriti*, the maternal prime substance of the Universe or nature in its vastest sense from which through the action of the three cosmic tendencies or *guṇas*, namely *satwa*, *rajas* and *tamas*, or goodness, passion and obscurity or the upward, expansive and downward tendencies, the whole cosmic domain is brought into being. There are twenty-five *tattvas* or principles whose knowledge forms the basis of the *Sāmkhya* system. There is first of all the four-fold division of things into the productive which is *Prakriti*, that which produces and is produced such as the intellect or *Buddhi*, that which is only produced such as the senses and the elements and finally that which neither produces nor is produced, that is, *Puruṣa*, the Universal Spirit which stands above and distinct from *Prakriti* and all its products.[25]

Furthermore, there is the more detailed division into the *tattvas*. Through the action of the *guṇas* which are present at all levels of cosmic reality, first the *Buddhi* or the intellect is generated and from *Buddhi* the principle of Egoism or *Ahankara*. From *Ahankara* there proceeds in turn the five subtle elements (*tanmatra*) which are the principles of the gross, corporeal elements. Also from *Ahankara* there come into being the eleven senses consisting of the five organs of sense, the five organs of action and the receptive and discriminative faculty (*manas*). From the subtle elements are produced the gross elements (*mahabuta*). Above this whole domain stands *Puruṣa* and the object of all sciences of nature is precisely for the soul to disentangle itself from the sense perceptions with which by mistake it identifies itself through the action of *manas* and *ahankara*.

The Universe itself which comes into being from the bosom of *Prakriti* or Nature is formed in such a way as to enable man to contemplate it in the metaphysical sense and thereby also achieve from it its separation or catharsis.[26] Moreover, once the spirit gains knowledge of nature, nature itself aids in this separation and withdraws from the scene. For as we read in the *Sāmkhya-*

Kārikā: 'As a dancer having exhibited herself on the stage, ceases to dance, so does nature (*Prakriti*) cease (to produce) when she has made herself manifest to the soul.'[27] Thus in the *Sāmkhya* system as in the *Vaiśeṣika* the knowledge of nature leads to the catharsis of the soul and its deliverance. Moreover, Nature itself is an aid in this process of realization and assists that spirit which is armed with discriminative knowledge.

This theme of relying upon nature in the task of spiritual realization is carried to its full conclusion in the practices connected with Tantra Yoga. In Tantrism the *Śakti* or feminine principle becomes the incarnation of all force and power in the Universe, and through the use of this very power, as if riding upon the waves of the sea, the Yogi seeks to pass beyond nature and the ocean of cosmic manifestation. In Tantrism there is an elaborate correspondence between man and the cosmos, the spinal column itself being called the Meru of the human body.[28] In fact, in the Tantric way or *sādhana*, the body and flesh of man and the living cosmos are the most fundamental elements.[29] The Universe is the 'body of the Lord'[30] and by dying and burying himself in its bosom, in the arms of nature as the Divine Mother, the Yogi finds his deliverance. The death and resurrection of the Yogi is very much like the *salve et coagula* of medieval Christian alchemists and in fact Tantrism became connected to alchemy in India and presents doctrines closely resembling those of the Western Hermeticists who also died in the maternal principle in order to be reborn in the spirit and sought the 'glorious body' as the Tantric Yogis sought the 'body of diamond' (*vajrayāna*). Tantrism in its connection with alchemy presents a most profound symbolic interpretation of nature closely associated with a spiritual way. Because of its close parallel with the Christian alchemical tradition it is a most effective means of recollecting ideas and doctrines which in the West have been long lost and forgotten.

Indian civilization also developed a great many sciences which were completely integrated within the structure of the tradition. The *Vedāngas*, consisting of the six sciences of phonetics (*śikṣā*);

ritual (*kalpa*); grammar (*vyākaraṇa*); etymology (*nirukta*); metrics (*chandas*) and astronomy (*jyotiṣa*) came into being at the end of the Brāhmaṇa period as inspired sciences (*smṛti*) as commentaries and complements of the divinely revealed Vedas (*śruti*).[31] *Vedānga* itself means literally 'limb of Veda' and implies that these sciences are an extension of the main body of the tradition contained in the Vedas. Below these sciences stands *Upaveda* (secondary Veda) consisting of medicine (*Ayur-veda*); military science (*Dhanur-veda*); music (*Gāndharva-veda*) and physics and mechanics (*Sthāpatya-veda*). Again these sciences are considered as an application of the principles contained in the Vedas to particular domains.[32] Even elements taken from Babylonian, Greek or Iranian sources were integrated into this traditional structure.

Furthermore, the sciences of arithmetic (*vyaka-ganita*); algebra (*bīja-ganita*) and geometry (*rekhā-ganita*) which influenced Muslim and Western science so greatly were closely tied to the metaphysical principles of Hinduism and also Buddhism as we see in the relation between the indefinite of algebra and the metaphysical Infinite, or the number zero first used in Indian arithmetic and the metaphysical doctrine of the void (*shunya*).[33] There was thus at every level an intricate and inextricable bond between the sciences and the metaphysical principles of the tradition. No science was ever cultivated outside the intellectual world of the tradition nor was nature ever profaned and made the subject of a purely secular study.

When we turn to Islam we find a religious tradition more akin to Christianity in its theological formulations yet possessing in its heart a gnosis or *sapientia* similar to the metaphysical doctrines of other Oriental traditions. In this, as in many other domains, Islam is the 'middle people', the *ummah wasatah* to which the Quran refers, in both a geographical and metaphysical sense. For this reason the intellectual structure of Islam and its cosmological doctrines and sciences of nature can be of the greatest aid in awakening certain dormant possibilities within Christianity.[34]

One finds in Islam an elaborate hierarchy of knowledge integrated by the principle of unity (*al-tawḥīd*) which runs as an axis through every mode of knowledge and also of being. There are juridical, social and theological sciences; and there are gnostic and metaphysical ones all derived in their principles from the source of the revelation which is the Quran. Then there have developed within Islamic civilization, elaborate philosophical, natural and mathematical sciences which became integrated into the Islamic view and were totally Muslimized. On each level of knowledge nature is seen in a particular light. For the jurists and theologians (*mutakallimūn*) it is the background for human action. For the philosopher and scientist it is a domain to be analyzed and understood. On the metaphysical and gnostic level it is the object of contemplation and the mirror reflecting suprasensible realities.[35]

Moreover, there has been throughout Islamic history an intimate connection between gnosis, or the metaphysical dimension of the tradition, and the study of nature as we also find it in Chinese Taoism. So many of the Muslim scientists like Avicenna, Quṭb al-Dīn Shīrāzī and Bahā' al-Dīn 'Āmilī were either practising Sufis or were intellectually attached to the illuminationist-gnostic schools. In Islam as in China observation of nature and even experimentation stood for the most part on the side of the gnostic and mystical element of the tradition while logic and rationalistic thought usually remained aloof from the actual observation of nature. There never occurred the alignment found in seventeenth-century science, namely a wedding of rationalism and empiricism which however was now totally divorced from the one experiment that was central for the men of old, namely experiment with oneself through a spiritual discipline.[36]

In Islam the inseparable link between man and nature, and also between the sciences of nature and religion, is to be found in the Quran itself, the Divine Book which is the Logos or the Word of God. As such it is both the source of the revelation which is the basis of religion and that macrocosmic revelation which is the

Universe. It is both the recorded Quran (*al-Qur'ān al-tadwīnī*) and the 'Quran of creation' (*al-Qur'ān al-takwīnī*) which contains the "ideas" or archetypes of all things. That is why the term used to signify the verses of the Quran or *āyah* also means events occurring within the souls of men and phenomena in the world of nature.[37]

Revelation to men is inseparable from the cosmic revelation which is also a book of God. Yet the intimate knowledge of nature depends upon the knowledge of the inner meaning of the sacred text or hermeneutic interpretation (*ta'wīl*).[38] The key to the inner meaning of things lies in *ta'wīl*, in penetrating from the outward (*ẓāhir*) to the inward (*bāṭin*) meaning of the Quran, a process which is the very opposite of the higher criticism of today. The search for the roots of knowledge in the esoteric meaning of a sacred text is also found in Philo and certain medieval Christian authors such as Hugo of St Victor and Joachim of Flora. Outside the mainstream of Christian orthodoxy it is found after the Renaissance in such writers as Swedenborg. It is precisely this tradition, however, that comes to an end in the West with the obliteration of metaphysical doctrines leaving the sacred text opaque and unable to answer the questions posed by the natural sciences. Left only with the external meaning of the Holy Scripture later Christian theologians could find no other refuge than a fundamentalism whose pathetic flight before nineteenth century science is still fresh in the memory.

By refusing to separate man and nature completely, Islam has preserved an integral view of the Universe and sees in the arteries of the cosmic and natural order the flow of divine grace or *barakah*. Man seeks the transcendent and the supernatural, but not against the background of a profane nature that is opposed to grace and the supernatural. From the bosom of nature man seeks to transcend nature and nature herself can be an aid in this process provided man can learn to contemplate it, not as an independent domain of reality but as a mirror reflecting a higher reality, a vast panorama of symbols which speak to man and have meaning for him.[39]

The purpose of man's appearance in this world is, according
to Islam, in order to gain total knowledge of things, to become
the Universal Man (*al-insān al-kāmil*), the mirror reflecting all the
Divine Names and Qualities.[40] Before his fall man was in the
Edenic state, the Primordial Man (*al-insān al-qadīm*); after his
fall he lost this state, but by virtue of finding himself as the central
being in a Universe which he can know completely, he can sur-
pass his state before the fall to become the Universal Man.
Therefore, if he takes advantage of the opportunity life has
afforded him, with the help of the cosmos he can leave it with
more than he had before his fall.

The purpose and aim of creation is in fact for God to come 'to
know' Himself through His perfect instrument of knowledge that
is the Universal Man. Man therefore occupies a particular position
in this world. He is at the axis and centre of the cosmic *milieu* at
once the master and custodian of nature. By being taught the
names of all things he gains domination over them, but he is
given this power only because he is the vicegerent (*khalīfah*)
of God on earth and the instrument of His Will. Man is given the
right to dominate over nature only by virtue of his theomorphic
make-up, not as a rebel against heaven.

In fact man is the channel of grace for nature; through his
active participation in the spiritual world he casts light into the
world of nature. He is the mouth through which nature breathes
and lives. Because of the intimate connection between man and
nature, the inner state of man is reflected in the external order.[41]
Were there to be no more contemplatives and saints, nature
would become deprived of the light that illuminates it and the
air which keeps it alive. It explains why, when man's inner
being has turned to darkness and chaos, nature is also turned
from harmony and beauty to disequilibrium and disorder.[42] Man
sees in nature what he is himself and penetrates into the inner
meaning of nature only on the condition of being able to delve
into the inner depths of his own being and to cease to lie merely
on the periphery of his being. Men who live only on the surface
of their being can study nature as something to be manipulated

nature a mirror : how we see nature
is how we see ourselves

this is one of the reasons Baha'u'llah appeared in an Islamic society

and dominated. But only he who has turned toward the inward dimension of his being can see nature as a symbol, as a transparent reality and come to know and understand it in the real sense.

In Islam, because of this very conception of man and nature, nature has never been considered as profane nor have the sciences of nature considered as *natura naturata* ever been studied without the remembrance of *natura naturans*. The presence of metaphysical doctrine and the hierarchy of knowledge enabled Islam to develop many sciences which exerted the greatest influence on Western science without these sciences disrupting the Islamic intellectual edifice. A man like Avicenna could be a physician and Peripatetic philosopher and yet expound his 'Oriental philosophy' which sought knowledge through illumination.[43] A Naṣīr al-Dīn Ṭūsī could be the leading mathematician and astronomer of his day, the reviver of Peripatetic philosophy, the author of the best known work on Shi'ite theology and an outstanding treatise on Sufism. His student Quṭb al-Dīn Shīrāzī could be the first person to explain correctly the cause of the rainbow and write the most celebrated commentary upon the *Theosophy of the Orient of Light* (*Hikmat al-ishrāq*) of Suhrawardī. The examples could be multiplied but these suffice to demonstrate the principle of the hierarchy of knowledge and the presence of a metaphysical dimension within Islam which satisfied the intellectual needs of men so that they never sought the satisfaction of their thirst for causality outside the religion as was to happen in the West during the Renaissance.

In fact it might be said that the main reason why modern science never arose in China or Islam is precisely because of the presence of metaphysical doctrine and a traditional religious structure which refused to make a profane thing of nature. Neither the 'Oriental bureaucratism' of Needham[44] nor any other social and economic explanation suffices to explain why the scientific revolution as seen in the West did not develop elsewhere. The most basic reason is that neither in Islam, nor India nor the Far East was the substance and stuff of nature so depleted of a sacramental and spiritual character, nor was the intellectual dimension of these traditions so enfeebled as to enable a purely secular science of nature and a secular philosophy to develop outside the matrix of the traditional intellectual orthodoxy.[45] Islam, which resembles Christianity in so many ways, is a perfect example of this truth, and the fact that modern science did not develop in its bosom is not the sign of decadence as some have claimed but of the refusal of Islam to consider any form of knowledge as purely secular and divorced from what it considers as the ultimate goal of human existence.

Before passing to the Christian tradition it is impossible not to mention briefly the case of the American Indians whose view concerning nature is a most precious message for the modern world. The Indians, especially of the Plains, did not develop an articulated metaphysics, but nevertheless they possess the profoundest metaphysical doctrines expressed in the most concrete and primordial symbols.[46] The Indian, who is something of a primordial monotheist, saw in virgin nature, in forests, trees, streams and the sky, in birds and buffalos, direct symbols of the spiritual world. With the strong symbolist spirit with which he was endowed he saw everywhere images of celestial realities. For him, as for other nomads, nature was sacred and there was a definite disdain of the artificialities of sedentary life. Virgin nature was for the Indian the cathedral in which he lived and worshipped. His desperate struggle against the white man was not only for a living space but also for a sanctuary. His civilization was so different from, and diametrically opposed to, that of the modern world that after living for thousands of years in nature, he left it in such a condition that today that very segment of nature must be turned into a national park in order to prevent it from becoming spoiled. When one sees the tracks of the Indian high in the Rocky Mountains, tracks which he crossed for millenia without disturbing the ambiance about him, one feels so strongly that the Indian was one who really walked gently upon the earth. For this, if for no other reason, the heritage of the American Indian contains a most precious message for the modern world.

If a day were to come when Christianity, rather than trying to convert the followers of Oriental religions, should also try to understand them and enter into an intellectual dialogue with them[47] then Oriental metaphysics, which is also in its essence the *philosophia perennis*, as well as the cosmological doctrines of the Oriental traditions (which could also be referred to as *cosmologia perennis*),[48] could act as a cause and occasion for recollection of elements forgotten in the Christian tradition. They could aid in restoring a spiritual vision of nature that would be able to provide the background for the sciences. Also, if we review the history of Christianity in the light of Oriental metaphysical and cosmological principles, some of which have been mentioned above, we shall discover a tradition of the study of nature which can act as the background for a new theological appraisal of the Christian vision of nature. It is in the light of these doctrines that we turn to a few representatives of this tradition in the history of Christianity.

In the Old Testament there are certain references to the participation of nature in the religious view of life, such as in the vision of Hosea in which God entered into covenant with beasts and plants in order to secure peace, or when Noah was ordered to preserve all animals whether they were clean or unclean, that is, irrespective of their usefulness or relation to man.[49] Likewise, virgin nature or wilderness is conceived as a place of trial and punishment as well as refuge and contemplation or as the reflection of paradise. This vision and tradition of the contemplative view of nature was to survive later in Judaism in both the Kabbalistic and Hassidim schools. As for the New Testament the death and resurrection of Christ is accompanied by a withering and rejuvenation of nature pointing to the cosmic character of Christ. St Paul also believed that all creation shares in the redemption.

In the West, however, the early Church as a reaction to paganism gradually became withdrawn and totally distinct from the world about it. Even the terms paradise and wilderness in their positive sense became connected solely with the Church and later with the monastery and the university as distinct institutions.[50] Gradually in the Western Church the selective character of salvation became more emphasized, and virgin nature and wilderness became interpreted as a domain of warfare and combat rather than of peace and contemplation. Even the geographic expansion of the Renaissance and the conquest of the New World were accomplished with this motif in mind.[51] In the Eastern Church, however, the contemplative view of nature was emphasized and made much more central. Nature was considered as a support for the spiritual life and the belief was held that all nature shares in salvation (*apokatastasis pantōn*) and the Universe is renovated and reconstructed by Christ in his second coming.

Among the early fathers also the Greek fathers like Origen, Irenaeus, Maximus the Confessor and Gregory of Nyssa who were so influential in the formation of Orthodox theology developed a theology of nature. Origen and Irenaeus are, particularly important since they applied the Logos doctrine not only to man and his religion but also to the whole of nature and all creatures. Their followers likewise showed much sympathy for a spiritual vision of nature.[52] The Latin fathers, however, did not for the most part show great interest in nature to the extent that the most famous among them, St Augustine, in the *City of God* considers nature as fallen and not yet redeemed.[53]

With the spread of Christianity into northern Europe, new ethnic groups entered the fold of Christianity who, far from being infected with the paganism of the Mediterranean world possessed a keen insight into the spiritual value of nature. Among Anglo-Saxons and Celts there was a strong awareness of the harmony between man and nature.[54] The Celtic monks sought after the *theoria* or vision of the cosmos as a divine theophany and went on pilgrimages in the hope of discovering harmony with God's creation. Some of the best nature poetry in the West is a product of their spiritual quest.[55]

It remained for a northerner, Johannes Scotus Erigena, to give the first complete metaphysical formulation of nature in the Latin Middle Ages. The ninth-century Irish scholar, who wrote commentaries on the Bible, in which he sought to reveal its inner meaning, as well as on Dionysus the Areopagite, is best known for his *De divisione naturae* dealing with God, creation and the return of creation to God. Some theologians and philosophers, who do not understand a metaphysical and cosmological doctrine of nature, are apt to accuse any doctrine of this kind of being pantheistic, but Erigena was fully aware of the Transcendent Origin of the Universe. Yet, for him all things in the Universe come from God and are created through Christ.[56] The first opening phrase of the Scriptures 'In the beginning God made the heaven and the earth' in fact means for Erigena the creation of all the primordial causes in Christ.[57]

Erigena, following Gregory of Nyssa, held a conception of matter according to which matter rather than being an opaque quantity is a combination of incorporeal qualities,[58] while form is all that gives existence to corporeal bodies and relates this domain to higher planes of existence. In the corporeal world as well as through all realms of creation the Trinity is present; the *essentia* of the Father as the source of existence, the *sapientia* of the Son as the source of wisdom and the *vita* of the Spirit as the life of all things in the Universe. And so man also has a triune nature comprised of the intellect (*nous*), reason (*logos*) and sense (*dianoia*).

Man stands in fact between the spiritual and material creations and partakes of the nature of both. In him the whole creation is contained in an essential rather than in a material or substantial sense.[59] Man is created in the image of God, yet as an animal, so that from one side the spiritual world is reflected in him and from the other the animal world. His destiny is inextricably tied to both the spiritual and natural worlds. That is why the *apokatastasis* or the final restoration means the passage of spiritualized nature to God and the restoration of all things including animals and trees.

In the light of this spiritual conception of nature, Erigena possessed a strong symbolic vision of things. Even in his astronomy, which in certain ways resembles the scheme of Tycho

Brahe, he gives a more eminent place to the Sun because of the symbolic nature of the Sun as the source of all existence and vitality, as the universal efficient cause in the cycle of the world.[60] He also expounds a doctrine of the states of being, and the inter-relation between levels in the hierarchy of existence. This inter-relation very much resembles the universal metaphysical doctrines of the Orient.[61]

Another eminent example of the Christian contemplative vision of nature is Saint Hildegard of Bingen, the visionary whose exposition of the structure of the cosmos is combined with re-markable miniatures going back to Saint Hildegard herself.[62] In her works the wedding of science and art so characteristic of the Middle Ages can be clearly seen. We observe a Christian cos-mography and cosmology expounded through the means of the sacred art of Christianity,[63] expressed in symbolic colours and forms which could be conveyed only through the medium of traditional art.

Saint Hildegard had a vision of the Universe, similar to that of Hugo of Saint Victor in which nature is totally in the domain of the Spirit manifesting itself in all products of nature. In her vision she is addressed by the Spirit in these remarkable words:

'I am that supreme and fiery force that sends forth all the sparks of life. Death hath no part in me, yet do I allot it, wherefore I am girt about with wisdom as with wings. I am that living and fiery essence of the divine substance that flows in the beauty of the fields. I shine in the water, I burn in the sun and the moon and the stars. Mine is that mysterious force of the invisible wind: I sustain the breath of all living. I breathe in the verdure, and in the flowers, and when the waters flow like living things, it is I. I found those columns that support the whole earth . . . I am the force that lies hid in the winds, from me they take their source, and as a man may move because he breathes, so doth a fire burn but by my blast. All these live because I am in them and am of their life. I am wisdom. Mine is the blast of the thundered word by which all things were made. I permeate all things that they may

not die. I am life.'[64] Here is a vision of nature still sacred and
spiritual before it became profane.

If Erigena expounded a metaphysical doctrine of nature and
Saint Hildegard a vision of a Christian cosmos expressed in
terms of Christian iconography and symbolism, Roger Bacon
was, as well as a mystic, a scientist and experimentor. He has
often been called a forerunner of modern science and along with
Robert Grosseteste the founder of the experimental method.[65]
What is usually forgotten is that Roger Bacon was also an illuminationist and Pythagorean who tried to cultivate the sciences of
nature in the matrix of supernatural knowledge, and conceived
of mathematics itself in a symbolic sense. He experimented, not
only with nature but also with the Holy Spirit within himself.[66]
He possessed a vision of the hierarchy of knowledge much like
that of the Muslim Avicenna whom he so greatly admired.
He cultivated the mathematical and natural sciences within the
fold of Christian intellectuality. It is unfortunate that his example
was not followed. Had he had successors, perhaps the Renaissance and seventeenth-century development of science wholly
outside the fold of Christianity would never have come about,
and the schism in Western civilization between science and
religion would have been prevented.[67] The fact that after Roger
Bacon, what came to be known later as science was cultivated
by rationalist and nominalist theologians rather than 'illumina-
tionists' and esoterists like Bacon, could only point to an inevitable divorce between science and religion.

We also find in the figure of St Francis of Assisi a most
startling reminder of the possibility of a reverential attitude towards nature within the aura of the Christian saintly life. His
life among the birds and beasts whom he addressed was a concrete example of the Christian belief that through holiness man
can gain a relationship with nature. This is a return to conditions
before the fall with its ensuing disruption of harmony between
man and nature.[68]

In the *Canticle of the Sun* and in many other sermons St
Francis displays a disinterested contemplative view of nature

outside all human utility. In his conversation with animals and even the elements, such as fire which he addressed when he was being cauterized, he illustrates the inner relation and intimacy that the saint gains with nature by virtue of his becoming identified with the Spirit that breathes within it.

Likewise, in Dante we see an eminent example of the integration of all knowledge, scientific, philosophical and theological into the total structure of Christianity. A synthesis whose highest meaning is revealed only to those who can unravel the anagogical meaning hidden within the *Divine Comedy*. The cosmos is a Christian one, the seven liberal arts correspond to so many levels of existence which the soul must realize, and the flight from the summit of the mount of Purgatory symbolizes the departure of the soul from the pinnacle of human perfection or the 'Lesser Mysteries', to states that are veritably transhuman and belong to the 'Greater Mysteries.'[69] The *Divine Comedy* contains in this cathedral of Christian intellectuality metaphysical and cosmological doctrines of lasting value not because of the symbolism of the Aristotelian astronomy which it employs, but because of the delineation of the structure of reality both externally and within the souls of men. This remains true independently of the symbolism used to express it. One must actually traverse the cosmos, or the levels of existence, to realize that the force that pervades all things is the 'love that moves the sun and the stars'.

Contemporary with Dante and following him during the next few centuries are the Christian alchemists, who integrated the Hermetic-alchemical doctrines of Alexandrian origin as later developed by Muslims into the perspective of Christianity. With men like Nicola Flamel who was a saintly and devout Christian and Basil Valentine, the attachment of alchemical doctrines to Christianity could no longer be denied. In the writings of these alchemists one finds, most significantly a vast doctrine of nature infused with the Christian spirit.

Alchemy is neither a premature chemistry nor a psychology in the modern sense, although both of these are to be found in alchemical writings.[70] Alchemy is a symbolic science of natural forms based on the correspondence between different planes of reality and making use of mineral and metal symbolism to expound a spiritual science of the soul. For alchemy, nature is sacred, and the alchemist is the guardian of nature considered as a theophany and reflection of spiritual realities.[71] A purely profane chemistry could come into being only when the substances of alchemy became completely emptied of their sacred quality. For this very reason, a re-discovery of the alchemical view of nature, without in any way denying the chemical sciences which deal with substances from another point of view, could reinstate the spiritual and symbolic character of the forms, colours and processes that man encounters throughout his life in the corporeal world.

Although after the Middle Ages the Christian tradition of the study of nature based on a metaphysical doctrine is more difficult to observe, it nevertheless continued until the nineteenth century. Men like John Ray and other Christian natural historians still went into the fields searching for the vestiges of God, the *vestigio Dei*. In Germany, the alchemist and theosopher, Jacob Böhme, one of the last Christian gnostics, continued the alchemical tradition of the study of nature. He spoke of the inner forces of nature, and of primordial nature in its pristine purity, still present here and now but which men cannot see because of turmoil and darkness within their souls that make them absent from it.[72] He invited men to seek to regain a vision of this pure and primordial nature. After him, Goethe in his *Farbenlehre* was to continue the interest in symbolism of colours and harmony within nature, while the followers of *Naturphilosophie* fought a losing battle against the mechanistic conception of nature. But by now even this battle was no longer fought from the camp of official Christianity.

The long tradition of the spiritual vision of nature, with the metaphysical doctrines upon which it is based, must again be brought to life within Christianity if the encounter of man and nature is not to result in complete disaster. Theologians and philosophers have been for the most part responsible, or at least have contributed during the past few centuries to making nature profane, thus setting the stage for its becoming profaned through the industrial revolution and the unending applications of modern sciences. They are thus responsible also for reinstating a more wholesome and integral attitude toward nature. Too many modern religious thinkers and theologians have put aside the question of nature and considered man's salvation with a total disregard for the rest of God's creation. In the present situation, however, human existence on this earth, not to mention man's ultimate salvation, has become a precarious matter. Because of this callous disregard for the rights of nature and other living things, it is high time for those who are really concerned with the state of man to turn to this long tradition of the study of nature within Christianity and to seek to restore the metaphysical doctrines of Christianity with the help of Oriental metaphysics. Only the revival of a spiritual conception of nature that is based on intellectual and metaphysical doctrines can hope to neutralize the havoc brought about by the applications of modern science and integrate this science itself into a more universal perspective.

the basis of a re-union of science & religion

NOTES TO CHAPTER III

1. 'A metaphysical doctrine is the incarnation in the mind of a universal truth. A philosophical system is a rational attempt to resolve certain questions which we put to ourselves.' See F. Schuon, *Spiritual Perspectives and Human Facts*, p. 11.

2. On Oriental metaphysics see R. Guénon, *La Métaphysique orientale*, Paris, 1951.

3. L. Giles, *The Sayings of Lao Tzŭ*, London, 1950, p. 22. Concerning Chinese metaphysical doctrines in general see Matgioi, *La Voie métaphysique*, Paris, 1956; and M. Granet, *La Pensée chinoise*, Paris, 1934.

4. *The Sacred Books of China, The Texts of Taoism* (trans. J. Legge), vol. I, New York, 1962, pp. 315–16.

5. J. Needham, *Science and Civilization in China*, vol. II, Cambridge, 1956, p. 50. Needham interprets this saying as proof of belief in scientific naturalism

and even makes a comparison with Lucretius. But there is a world of difference between the Hellenistic – Roman 'naturalism' and 'naturism' of
other traditions in which the substance of nature has not become profane
but acts as a means of conveying grace.

6. *The Sayings of Lao Tҳŭ*, p. 23.

7. Needham, *op. cit.*, pp. 36 ff.

8. *The Sacred Books of China, The Texts of Taoism*, Part I, p. 342.

9. Chuang-Tzu referring to the sages writes: '(Such men) by their stillness
become sages; and by their movement, kings. Doing nothing, they are
honoured; in their plain simplicity, no one in the world can strive with them
(for the palm of) excellence. The clear understanding of the virtue of Heaven
and Earth is what is called "The Great Root", and "The Great Origin"—
they who have it are in harmony with Heaven, and so they produce all
equable arrangements in the world;—they are those who are in harmony
with men.' *Ibid.*, p. 332.

10. Quoted in Fung Yu-Lan, *A History of Chinese Philosophy* (trans. D.
Bodde), vol. I, Princeton, 1952, p. 224.

11. The Sayings of *Chuang Chou* (trans. J. Ware), New York, 1963, p. 88.

12. See Needham, *op. cit.*, pp. 49 f.

13. *Ibid.*, p. 51.

14. *The Sacred Books of China; The Texts of Taoism*, Part I, pp. 297–8.

15. This point has been emphasized in several works by Needham: 'Em-
bodied therefore in the common present-day name for a Taoist temple
[kuan] is the ancient significance of the observation of Nature, and since in
their beginnings magic, divination and science were inseparable, we cannot
be surprised that it is among the Taoists that we have to look for most of
the roots of Chinese scientific thought.' 'The Pattern of Nature-Mysticism
and Empiricism in the Philosophy of Science, Third Century B.C. China,
Tenth Century A.D. Arabia, and Seventeenth Century A.D. Europe, in
Science, Medicine and History, Essays in Honor of Charles Singer (ed. E.
Ashworth Underwood), London, 1953, p. 361.

16. 'In Asia, Shamanism properly so-called is met with not only in Siberia,
but also in Tibet (in the form of Bön-po) and in Mongolia, Manchuria and
Korea. The pre-Buddhist Chinese tradition, with its Confucian and Taoist
branches, is attached to the same traditional family, and the same applies to
Japan, where Shamanism has given rise to the specifically Japanese *Shinto*
tradition. Characteristic of all these doctrines is a complementary opposition
of Heaven and Earth, and a cult of Nature . . .' Schuon, *Light on the Ancient
Worlds*, p. 72.

17. This in fact is the way that incomparable scholar of Hinduism and of Oriental metaphysics and art in general, A. K. Coomaraswamy, translated *māya*.

18. Of the immense number of works on Hinduism in the European languages very few have understood the proper Hindu point of view and expressed the view of the tradition itself. As far as the metaphysical doctrines of Hinduism and the structure of this tradition is concerned see R. Guénon, *Introduction to the Study of the Hindu Doctrines* (trans. M. Pallis), London, 1945; R. Guénon, *Man and His Becoming, according to the Vedanta* (trans. R. Nicholson), London, 1945; F. Schuon, *The Language of the Self*; and the many works of A. K. Coomaraswamy especially *Hinduism and Buddhism*, New York (n.d.). See also the lucid expositions of M. Eliade and H. Zimmer.

19. There are of course exceptions as those in the seventeenth century who spoke of the atomism of Moses and related the atomistic view to the Hebrew prophet himself.

20. 'The bondage of the world is due to false knowledge which consists in thinking as my own self that which is not myself, namely, body senses, manas, feelings and knowledge; when once the true knowledge of the six padārthas, and as Nyāya says, of the proofs, the objects of knowledge, and of the other logical categories of inference is attained, fasle knowledge is destroyed.' S. Dasgupta, *A History of Indian Philosophy*, vol. I, Cambridge, 1922, p. 365.

21. *Padārthadharmasangraha* of Praçastapāda (trans. M. G. Jha), Allahabad, 1916, p. 13.
The same text asserts: 'Here also the declaration that the knowledge of similarity etc. is the means of highest beatitude implies that such beatitude is brought about by a true knowledge of the categories themselves; as there could be no knowledge of the said similarity etc. independently of the categories.' p. 15.

22. *The Sacred Books of the Hindus* (ed. B. D. Basu), vol. VI, *The Vaiśeṣika Sūtras of Kaṇādā* (trans. Nandalal Sinha), Allahabad, 1923, p. 2.

23. 'From the injurious effect of the threefold kinds of pain (arises) a desire to know the means of removing it (pain). If, from the visible (means of removing it), this (desire) should seem to be superfluous, it is not so, for these are neither absolutely complete nor abiding.' *The Sankhya Karika of Iswar Krishna* (trans. by J. Davies), Calcutta, 1957, p. 6.
We have made some use for this analysis of Sāṃkhya of the Persian work of D. Shayegan, which is now in press (Tehran Univ. Press). Concerning the Sāṃkhya system see A. B. Keith, *Sāṃkhya System*, Calcutta, 1949 and B. N. Seal (Vrajendranātha-Ṣila), *Positive Sciences of the Ancient Hindus*, London, 1915.

24. 'The way of eradicating the root of sorrow is thus the practical enquiry of the Sāmkhya philosophy.' Dasgupta, *op. cit.*, p. 265.

25. This four-fold division has a startling resemblance to the *De divisione naturae* of Erigena.

26. 'It is that the soul may be able to contemplate Nature, and to become entirely separated from it, that the union of both is made, as of the halt and the blind, and through that (union) the universe is formed.' *The Sankhya Karika*, p. 34.

27. *Ibid.*, p. 67. The commentary *Tattva-Kaumudī* moreover adds, 'as a qualified servant accomplishes the good of his unqualified master, through purely unselfish motives, without any benefit to himself; so does Nature endowed with the three Attributes, benefit the Spirit without any good in return to herself. Thus the pure unselfishness of Nature's motives is established.' *Tattva-Kaumudī* of Vāchaspati Miśra (trans. G. Jha), Bombay, 1896, p. 104.

28. See Sir J. Woodruffe, *Introduction to Tantra Śastra*, Madras, 1956, pp. 34–5.

29. See M. Eliade, *Yoga, Immortality and Freedom*, New York, 1958, p. 204.

30. See Sir J. Woodruffe, *The World As Power*, Madras, 1957, p. 3.

31. See *Cultural Heritage of India*, vol. I, Calcutta, 1958, pp. 264–2 (chapter on the *Vedangas* by V. M. Apte).

32. Concerning the *Upavedas* see Guénon, *Introduction to the Study of the Hindu Doctrines*, Chapter VIII.

33. On the relation between zero and the centre of the cosmic wheel as well as the void see A. K. Coomaraswamy, '*Kha* and Other Words Denoting "Zero", in Connection with the Metaphysics of Space', *Bull. School of Oriental Studies*, vol. VII, 1934, pp. 487–97.

34. Concerning cosmological doctrines in Islam see S. H. Nasr, *An Introduction to Islamic Cosmological Doctrines*. As for the Islamic sciences themselves see S. H. Nasr, *Science and Civilization in Islam*.

35. See S. H. Nasr, *Islamic Studies*, Beirut, 1966, chapter V, 'The Meaning of nature in Various Intellectual Perspectives in Islam' and Chapter XIII 'Contemplation and Nature in the Perspective of Sufism'.

36. Even in the Renaissance many of the observers and experimenters far from being rationalistic were steeped in the Kabbalistic, Rosicrucian, or other mystical schools of the period as shown so clearly by W. Pagel in his 'Religious Motives in the Medical Biology of the Seventeenth Century'. *Bull. History of Medicine*, 1935, vol. II, no. 2, pp. 97–128; no. 3, pp. 213–31;

no. 4, pp. 265–312. As for the case of Taoism see Needham, *Science and Civilization in China*, vol. II, pp. 91 ff. in addition to his article already cited.

37. In fact the Quran asserts, 'We shall show them our portents upon the horizons and within themselves, until it be manifest unto them that it is the Truth'. (XLI; 53) (Pickthall translation); see Nasr, *An Introduction to Islamic Cosmological Doctrines*, p. 6.

38. See H. Corbin (with the collaboration of S. H. Nasr and O. Yahya), *Histoire de la philosophie islamique*, Paris, 1964, pp. 13–30; and H. Corbin, 'L'intériorisation du sens en herméneutique soufie iranienne', *Eranos Jahrbuch*, XXVI, Zurich, 1958. See also S. H. Nasr, *Ideals and Realities of Islam*, London, 1966, chapter II.

39. 'Nor is there anything which is more than a shadow. Indeed, if a world did not cast down shadows from above, the worlds below it would at once vanish altogether, since each world in creation is no more than a tissue of shadows entirely dependent on the archetypes in the world above. Thus the foremost and truest fact about any form is that it is a symbol, so that when contemplating something in order to be reminded of its higher realities the traveller is considering that thing in its universal aspect which alone explains its existence.' Abu Bakr Siraj Ed-Din, *The Book of Certainty*, London, 1952, p. 50.

40. On this capital doctrine see al-Jīlī, *De l'homme universel* (trans. T. Burckhardt), Lyon, 1953; and T. Burckhardt, *An Introduction to Sufi Doctrine* (trans. D. M. Matheson), Lahore, 1959.

41. 'In considering what the religions teach, it is essential to remember that the outside world is as a reflection of the soul of man . . .' *The Book of Certainty*, p. 32. 'The state of the outer world does not merely correspond to the general state of men's souls; it also in a sense depends on that state, since man himself is the pontiff of the outer world. Thus the corruption of man must necessarily affect the whole, . . .' *Ibid.*, p. 33.

42. A traditional Muslim would see in the bleakness and ugliness of modern industrial society and the ambiance it creates an outward reflection of the darkness within the souls of men who have created this order and who live in it.

43. See H. Corbin, *Avicenna and the Visionary Recital* (trans. W. Trask), New York, 1961; and S. H. Nasr, *Three Muslim Sages*, Chapter I; *An Introduction to Islamic Cosmological Doctrines*, pp. 177 ff.

44. See J. Needham, 'Science and Society in East and West', *Centaurus*; vol. 10, no. 3, 1964, pp. 174–97.

45. By orthodoxy we do not mean simply following the exoteric and literal

interpretation of a religion but to possess the right doctrine (*orthos-doxia*) on both the exoteric and esoteric levels. see F. Schuon, 'Orthodoxy and Intellectuality', in *Language of The Self*, Madras, 1959, pp. 1–14.

46. Concerning the metaphysical teachings of the Indians see J. Brown, *The Sacred Pipe*, Norman, 1953; also F. Schuon, 'The Shamanism of North American Indians', in *Light on the Ancient World*, pp. 72–8.

47. As far as the Islamic world is concerned, with a few rare exceptions, there has been no intellectual contact with Christianity since the Middle Ages.

48. Concerning this perennial cosmology see T. Burckhardt, *Cosmologia Perennis, Kairos*, vol. VI, no. 2, 1964, pp. 18–32.
This is not to say of course that there are no differences in the role and meaning of nature in the various traditions cited. But there is enough agreement on principles and on the metaphysical significance of nature to warrant the use of the term *'cosmologia perennis'*.

49. Williams, *Wilderness and Paradise in Christian Thought*, introduction p. x.

50. 'The corresponding term to *paradise*, in the sense of the Garden of the Great King of the universe, will in due course be applied provisionally to the Church, then more exclusively to the disciplined monastery alone, then to the school growing out of the Church and monastery, namely, the medieval university, and at length in the New World to the theological seminary as the seedbed of missionaries and ministers.' *Ibid.*, p. 6.

51. This development has been fully traced in Williams, *Wilderness and Paradise*.

52. Basil of Neo-Caesarea, an Origenist, writes in his *Hexaemeron*: 'A single blade of grass is enough to occupy your whole mind as you contemplate the skill that produced it', and lectures on nature as the handiwork of God. See Raven, *Natural Religion and Christian Theology I, Science and Religion*, p. 47, where this saying is quoted.

53. For the attitude of St Augustine and the early Church as well as later Christianity toward nature see Raven, *op. cit.*

54. Williams, *Paradise and Wilderness*, pp. 46 ff.

55. 'The pilgrimage of the Irish monk was therefore not merely the restless search of an unsatisfied romantic heart, it was a profound and existential tribute to the realities perceived in the very structure of the world, and of men, and of their being: a sense of ontological and spiritual dialogue between man and creation in which spiritual and bodily realities interweave and interlace themselves like manuscript illuminations in the *Book of Kells* . . . Better perhaps than the Greeks, some of the Celtic monks arrived at the purity of that *theoria physike* which sees God not in the essences or *logoi*

of things, but in a hierophanic cosmos: hence the marvellous vernacular nature poetry of the 6th and 7th century Celtic hermits.' T. Merton, 'From Pilgrimage to Crusade', *Tomorrow*, Spring, 1965, p. 94.

56. Erigena followed the view of Clement of Alexandria who asserted, 'The Son is neither absolutely one, as one; nor yet many, as parts; but one, as all things; for from Him are all things; and He is the circle of all powers collected and united into one'. *Stromata*, IV, 635.9 quoted in H. Bett, *Johannes Scotus Erigena, a Study in Mediaeval Philosophy*, Cambridge, 1925, p. 32.

57. *Ibid.*, p. 40.

58. 'The space of a point is not a space perceived by the senses, but a space understood by the intellect. So a point is incorporeal, and the beginning of lines; a line is incorporeal and the beginning of surfaces; a surface is incorporeal and the beginning of solidity, and solidity is the perfection of matter. Matter, therefore, is really a combination of incorporeal qualities. It is form which constitutes and contains all material bodies, and form is incorporeal.' *Ibid.*, p. 46.

59. 'As man is the middle point between the extremes of spiritual and corporeal, a unique union of soul and body, it is natural to suppose that every creature, visible and invisible, from one extreme to the other, is created in man, and that all are reunited and reconciled in man.' *Ibid.*, p. 58.

60. Concerning his astronomy see E. von Erhardt – Siebold and R. von Erhardt, *The Astronomy of Johannes Scotus Erigena*, Baltimore, 1940 and their *Cosmology in the 'Annotations in Marcianum'*, Baltimore, 1940.

61. See G. B. Burch, *Early Medieval Philosophy*, New York, 1951 and 'The Christian non-dualism of Scotus Erigena', *Philosophical Quarterly*, vol. 26, 1954, pp. 209–14, where some comparisons are made, more from the philosophical than the properly metaphysical point of view.

62. The scientific works of St Hildegard are contained in *Scivias* and *Liber divinorum operum simplicis nominis* whose Luccan ms. contains the beautiful miniatures.

63. There is a close link between cosmology and sacred art in that both select from the multitude of forms certain elements that reflect a particular religious and ethnic genius. See T. Burckhardt, *Von Wesen Heiliger Kunst in den Welt Religionen*, 1955. For Christian cosmography in its relation to art see J. Baltrusaitis, *Cosmographie chrétienne dans l'art du moyen-âge*, Paris, 1939.

64. C. Singer, *Studies in the History and Method of Science*, Oxford, vol. I, 1917, 'The Scientific Views and Visions of Saint Hildegard', p. 33.

At the end of her life St Hildegard wrote. 'And now that I am over seventy years old my spirit according to the will of God soars upward in vision to the highest heaven and to the farthest stretch of the air and spreads itself among different peoples to regions exceeding far from me here, and thence I can behold the changing clouds and the mutations of all created things; for all these I see not with the outward eye or ear, nor do I create them from the cogitations of my heart ... but within my spirit, my eyes being open, so that I have never suffered any terror when they left me.' *Ibid.*, p. 55.

65. See A. Crombie, *Robert Grosseteste and the Origins of Experimental Science*, Oxford, 1955.

66. Referring to Roger Bacon A. E. Taylor writes, 'There is at bottom no difference between natural and supernatural knowledge. His serious theory is that all certain knowledge is experimental, but experiment is of two kinds, experiment made on external nature, the source of certainty in natural science, and experimental acquaintance with the work of the Holy Spirit within the soul, the source of the knowledge of heavenly things which culminates in the vision of God.' *European Civilization*, vol. III, London, 1935, p. 827.

67. F. Picavet writes that if the path of R. Bacon had been followed, 'there would have been no room for a Renaissance wholly separated from Catholicism, nor for an open struggle and total rupture between theology, philosophy and science'. Quoted by C. Raven, *Science and Religion*, p. 87.

68. 'Whatever the actual episodes may have been, it is significant that both the saints and the hagiographer felt that only through the recovery of pristine holiness could man help undo the ferocity brought into the world by man's primordial disobedience in the first Paradise.' Williams, *Wilderness and Paradise*, p. 42.

69. See R. Guénon, *L'Esotérisme de Dante*, Paris, n.d.

70. Whatever service the works of C. G. Jung may have rendered to make alchemy better known, they are inadequate in that they limit alchemy to a psychology that is devoid of a transcendent and spiritual origin for the symbols that appear to the human psyche.

71. See Burckhardt, *De Alchemie. Sinn und Weltbild* where examples of Christian alchemists are given; see also M. Eliade, *The Forge and the Crucible*, New York, 1956.

72. Concerning Böhme, see A. Koyré, *La Philosophie de Jacob Boehme*, Paris, 1928; and the section devoted to Böhme in *Hermès*, 3, Winter, 1964–65.

Chapter 4

Certain Applications to the Contemporary Situation

If there were to be a re-discovery of metaphysics and the re-establishment of a metaphysical tradition in the West tied to the appropriate spiritual methods and within the fold of Christianity, then one could hope for the rejuvenation of both theology and philosophy, and the birth of a criterion to judge and regulate the sciences. In the light of this restoration, theology could expand so as to embrace also a theology of nature. Philosophy, rather than being a footnote to the fruits of experimental science, could regain its independence and become at once a judge and critic of the methods and hypotheses of science. Further, the metaphysical doctrines themselves could act as the immutable centre around which all intellectual effort rotates and whose applications to different domains determines the path to be followed in each.

The first result of the application of the principles in question would be the creation of standards by which to judge the results and implications of different sciences; not to dictate to them, but to point out the boundary within which each science functions, and the meaning that its discoveries possess beyond those borders. It would be, in short, the creation of the means to criticize science and its applications creatively and fruitfully. It is indeed curious that in the modern world, where everything is criticized and questioned, where there are critics of art, of literature, of politics, of philosophy and even of religion there are no critics of science.[1] Even if occasional critics are found they are expelled from the respected academic and scholarly community and do not occupy at all the same status as the art or literary critic.

Some might say that whereas art and literature, or even politics and religion, are a matter of personal choice and taste, science is validated by its positive applications which no one can deny or criticize. But this objection is false not only in that it neglects the objective norms and principles of religion, art and other non-scientific domains, but also completely misinterprets the theoretical structure of science and its practical applications in technology and engineering. Nineteenth-century inventors of the steam engine used a physical theory which today is considered as scientifically false.[2] In fact most of the inventors up to very recent times have been, for the most part, ignorant of the science of their day and have applied theories that have proved to be false. Moreover, even today a physical or chemical theory can change while its application continues untouched. The success of applied science, therefore, is no reason for accepting the infallibility of the scientific theories involved. There should be an intelligent and conscious criticism of science and its implications, both for those involved in the sciences, and most of all for those who are the recipients of the popularized versions of scientific theories. The philosophy of science has in certain cases tried to point to the lack of logical consistency in some scientific definitions and methods. But having surrendered itself to the fruits of the experimental and analytical methods, it cannot itself be an independent judge of modern science.

The restoration of a complete metaphysical doctrine could also serve the all important function of delineating once again the level and stages of reality, and of presenting the anatomy of being in its multiple grades and states. With Descartes, reality in Western philosophy became reduced to mind and matter, and through the later generation of philosophers such as Malebranche, Spinoza and even Leibnitz this impoverishment of reality became an accepted fact and serves as the background of science and especially mathematical physics to this day. The long debate between idealists and realists is no more than the attempt to answer a question which from the metaphysical point of view is ill posed to start with.

In this background of the reduction of reality to two totally distinct and separate substances, nature has perforce become reduced to quantity, and the human microcosm has itself lost its tripartite structure of spirit (*spiritus*), soul (*anima*) and body (*corpus*) to become a mind mysteriously connected to a body with which it has no common measure. Likewise, all that belongs to the psychic and spiritual domains has been banished from nature.

A re-discovery of the anatomy of being which places each mode of existence, the corporeal, the psychic and the spiritual in its place, to mention the most fundamental divisions, can also serve to clarify certain phenomena which modern science is forced to reject but in which society as a whole displays great interest. Such are for example the phenomena connected with the subtle or psychic substance which has a cosmic as well as a human component. The multitude of phenomena connected with this order are left for occultists to deal and play with. By being banished from the official scientific world-view they have not by any means been made to disappear from man's life and society. Their very exclusion from the domain of reality accepted by science has both impoverished the present conception of the total science of things, and led to the cultivation of dangerous practices by all kinds of occultist organizations that only increase from day to day. One could say that modern man has not experienced the psychic substance within nature to the same extent as men of other ages, due to a difference of his own make up as well as the constitution of the ambiance around him. However, to the extent that he has had experiences of this kind, they are relegated to a category whose negation by official scientific circles does not in any way make them any less real, or their effect on society any less felt. The exponential rise in societies and publications associated with spiritism and the like, amidst the supposedly most scientific age of human history should at least be a source of reflection.

Likewise, the delineation of the grades of reality could again elucidate and clarify the traditional sciences such as alchemy, astrology, etc., whose true significance lies in their symbolic meaning and the correspondence and concordance between different stages of reality. The loss of this metaphysical knowledge has made these sciences appear as superstitions, contrary to both reason and experience. Again, their rejection by the official scientific view has not caused them to disappear by any means. There are an astounding number of works published on them every year, and in such a citadel of rationalism as France there are more works published on the occult sciences every year than on many branches of modern science. With a total disregard for the symbolic meaning of these sciences—whose real sense has long been forgotten—this enormous interest only fosters superstition in the true sense of the word and adds to the confusion of thought. No amount of attack by scientists can help to overcome or stop it. Only a metaphysical knowledge of the grades of reality, and the correspondences based on them, could again place these sciences in their proper perspective and neutralize the harm that is brought about through a misunderstanding of their teachings.[3]

This function of metaphysics is closely related to its role as the background for a philosophy of nature into which the modern sciences could be integrated. We have already alluded to the lack of a comprehensive philosophy of nature today, and the need for precisely such a philosophy. A re-vitalized intellectual tradition based on a real metaphysical knowledge could firstly free philosophy from total slavery to the senses, the fruit of experimentation and empiricism, and secondly could help in the creation of a philosophy of nature which would outline the anatomy of nature and the different sciences that could be associated with it.

This does not mean the imposition of a restriction from above on a particular science or a change of the method of, let us say, chemistry from induction to deduction. It means rather, the creation of a total vision of nature which would place the findings of any particular science such as physics or chemistry within a larger scheme of knowledge and relate the discoveries of each science to knowledge as a whole. Today, all kinds of philosophical conclusions are made concerning physical or astronomical theories and discoveries, often with total neglect for the limitations and assumptions originally made by the scientists. With Kant, physics became the source of philosophy and there developed a physicism very much similar to the earlier mathematicism of Descartes. With a real philosophy of nature there would be an independent matrix within which the implications of different sciences could be tested and tried and their meaning made known without the aberrations which so often accompany philosophical interpretations of scientific theories today.

Metaphysical doctrine could also aid in the re-discovery of virgin nature by removing the strangulating hold that rationalism has placed upon man's vision of nature. There is a need to re-discover virgin nature as a source of truth and beauty in the most strict intellectual sense and not merely in the sentimental one. Nature must be seen as an affirmation and aid in the spiritual life and even a means of grace rather than the obscure and opaque reality it has come to be considered.[4] It must once again become a means of recollection of Paradise and the state of felicity which man naturally seeks.[5]

The re-discovery of virgin nature does not mean a flight of individualistic and Promethean man toward nature. While in the state of rebellion against Heaven man carries with him his own limitations even when he turns to nature. These limitations veil the spiritual message of nature for him so that he derives no benefit from it. It is in this way that the modern urbanized citizen in search of virgin nature takes with him those very elements that destroy nature and thereby he destroys the very thing he is searching for. Nor is the re-discovery of virgin nature a return to paganism from a theological point of view. There is a profound difference between the paganism of the Mediterranean world, this idolatry of created things against which Christianity has fought, and the 'naturism' of the northern European people for whom nature possessed a symbolic and spiritual significance. The re-discovery of virgin nature with the aid of traditional principles would mean a reunification of the symbolic meaning of natural forms and the development of a spiritual sympathy (*sym-pathia*) for nature which has nothing to do with either ancient paganism and idolatry or the modern individualistic revolt.[6] It would mean the restoration of man to his home in the cosmos.[7]

Such an attitude could also aid in cultivating a sense of love for nature which is the very antithesis of the prevalent attitude of modern man as the conqueror and enemy of nature. Few realize that by the very fact that nature is finite its boundaries cannot be pushed back indefinitely. Man simply cannot continue to conquer and dominate nature endlessly without expecting a reaction on the part of nature to re-establish the equilibrium destroyed by man. A spiritual sense of nature could, at least to a certain extent, ameliorate this existing attitude and the danger inherent in it and provide a remedy for the acute illness from which the modern world suffers. The suffering is brought about by the excessive application of technology and the waging of war both of which are united in their enmity and aggression against nature. The bitter fruit of the purely antagonistic attitude toward nature is so evident today that few can afford to overlook any means that might provide a solution to it.

As for the modern sciences of nature, a metaphysical science rooted in the intellect, revelation, and a philosophy of nature based upon it could provide both criticism and evaluation of scientific discoveries and hypotheses. The two would be complementary in as much as the modern sciences deal with detailed knowledge and metaphysics with the ultimate knowledge of things. At the same time metaphysics, being independent of science, could examine its presuppositions and act as its independent critic and judge.[8]

Nature is altogether richer than the knowledge which physics arrives at through its quantitative methods which are selective in both their data and the interpretation of these data.[9] Physics is a science of nature limited by the very selections it makes of external reality very much like the ichthyologist with a particular size of net whose example Eddington has made well known.[10]

*The fact that an experiment works is no proof
– that the theory behind it is correct ... just as
working inventions can be based on wrong theories ...*

Man and Nature

Likewise, the very fact that its conclusions are based on experiments implies that their validity holds only within the conditions of those experiments.[11] Physics then, like the other sciences of nature is *a* particular science of things, legitimate within its own assumptions and limitations, but it is not *the* only valid science of the natural world. It is only one possible science of nature among others.[12] Physics gives us some knowledge of the physical world but not all the knowledge that is needed, especially as far as the integral relation of man and nature is concerned.[13] The very qualities, forms and harmonies which physics leaves aside from its quantitative point of view, very far from being accidental or negligible, are the aspects most closely tied to the ontological root of things. That is why the application of a science which neglects these elements causes disequilibrium and brings about disorder and ugliness, especially in a world where other sciences of nature do not exist and where there is no wisdom or *sapientia* which could place the quantitative sciences in their proper position in the total scheme of knowledge.

Due to the lack of this total science it is also forgotten that phenomena participate on several cosmic levels and their reality is not exhausted by a single level of existence, least of all the material one.[14] In the same way that a living tissue can be made the object of study of biology, chemistry and physics or a mountain the subject of geology, geophysics and geomorphology, so does each phenomenon lend itself to study from different points of view and on different planes of existence. For this reason there is no single science of nature but different pictures and visions of the world each valid to the extent that it can depict a certain aspect of cosmic reality. It is not true to say that the sun is only incandescent gas, although this is an aspect of its reality. It is also as true to say that the sun is the symbol of the intelligible principle in the Universe and this element is as much an aspect of its ontological reality as the physical features discovered by modern astronomy.

Seen in the perspective of the total science of nature, the immediate appearance of nature with the solid earth below, the blue sky above and the sun moving regularly across the firmament, the Aristotelian and the medieval cosmologies based on the appearance of things as well as the Newtonian and relativistic views of the world are all, from a certain point of view, true. Mathematically speaking, the theory of relativity is more general and exact, the Newtonian physics a special case of it, and medieval cosmology and physics only a rough, qualitative estimate. But the mathematical aspect of things is not everything. It is concerned only with their quantitative dimension, not with the qualitative which connects each being ontologically to its source. That is why each picture of the world as it becomes mathematically more exact also becomes symbolically less direct and farther removed from the metaphysical knowledge which the immediate appearance of nature conveys through its symbolism.[15] Yet, as long as any conceptual scheme in physics is capable of explaining phenomena coherently, it possesses some symbolic significance that transcends its factual meaning by its very correlation with an aspect of objective reality. Yet it must always be remembered that the success of any particular theory in explaining phenomena mathematically, no matter how exact, does not in the least invalidate the symbolic significance of other pictures of the world, which are based either on the direct appearances of things or on cosmological doctrines reflecting metaphysical principles.

As a criticism of philosophies and general conclusions based on physics, one could point to the exclusivity accorded to mathematical logic as if this were the only form of logic. What is mathematically satisfactory is considered to be true even if it violates the principles of intelligence and the logic connected with the imaginative faculty. But there is no reason whatsoever to limit all the intellectual faculties to mathematical logic and overlook the demands of the rest. So much of modern philosophy that relies on physics, and so many generalizations within physics itself, are based on this unconscious mathematicism which Cartesian philosophy bestowed upon mathematical physics, and which has become accentuated in contemporary science. In the domains of both micro- and astrophysics direct contact with objective reality has been removed, leaving only an abstract mathematical model as the means of analysing the structure of matter.

The conception of matter based solely on mathematical criteria leads, even in the domain of modern physics, to certain conclusions which philosophically and metaphysically seem incongruent and in certain cases contradictory. A purely mathematical physics may be able to afford the privilege of remaining unconcerned about such matters, but for a total science of nature, and especially generalizations of the world view of physics, these questions are of great significance. For example, one often speaks of fields of force or waves which possess energy and have specific characteristics but which move in a vacuum. Now, mathematically such a model may be a convenient one upon which to base calculations, but physically one cannot accept a total void as exhibiting characteristics. A void is nothing and what does not exist cannot exhibit anything.[16] Likewise, the discontinuity exhibited in matter at the sub-atomic level, with all the significance that Planck's constant has, does not invalidate a substratum of continuity which so many other natural phenomena, especially light, demand. The ambivalent nature of light points if anything to a continuous underlying substance, what traditional cosmology calls the ether, which also exhibits a discontinuous aspect by virtue of its being indistinct. The debate in this domain today, if one glances at the principles involved, is not very much different from that of the followers of hylomorphism and atomism in the Middle Ages and in Antiquity.

Likewise, in the theory of relativity one speaks of the absolute speed of light and the dependence of the time-space structure upon it. However satisfactory the Lorenz transformations and generalizations of Einstein concerning the theory of relativity may be mathematically, it is not possible to accept the conceptions of time and space, the notion of simultaneity and other aspects of this theory as being exclusive and as exhausting the nature of physical reality as such. The Euclidian space from which we begin continues to possess its validity and reality, not only as an approximation or special case of non-Euclidian geometries, but independently of them. In the same way, conceptions of time and space based on our immediate apprehension of them are valid not only approximately but exactly and completely. It is the abstract time-space structure that is their extension, attained by pursuing a particular train of thought based on certain presumptions upon the nature of physical reality. In all these cases metaphysics and an independent philosophy of nature would not invalidate physical theories but show exactly what they mean. They would point out the reality of those elements of the physical world which the highly abstract and mathematical models of modern physics have left aside. Further, they would point out the fact that quantum mechanics, the theory of relativity and particle physics deal, without doubt, with an aspect of the physical world, but would add that the picture derived from them is not that of the whole of physical reality but only its most quantitative and material aspect. Moreover, when this quantitative analysis of matter is carried to its limit it leads to disorder and dissolution bordering upon what the medieval philosophers called *materia prima*. The disorder and dissolution accompanying the explosion of thermonuclear devices in fact point to the same conclusion.

Metaphysics would distinguish carefully between facts assembled diligently by scientists and hypotheses, many unproven, which are used to integrate these facts into some meaningful pattern. A total and complete science of things would be able to judge these hypotheses and their implications. It would stand as a standard with respect to which modern science would be compared and judged.[17] It would criticize the vulgarizations of science and the popular philosophies based upon them as well as the contradictions within the sciences themselves. Moreover, this would be carried out not only in physics but in all sciences such as biology and psychology where even more than in physics wild conjectures are often paraded as scientifically proven facts.

With psychology and some of its misdeeds and shortcomings we are not concerned, although errors in the Jungian interpretation of traditional sciences and symbols definitely need to be pointed out.[18] In the domain of biology, however, one can hardly avoid mentioning the theory of evolution which has become fashionable in this century and has dominated nearly every branch of knowledge from astronomy to history itself. We have become accustomed to speaking about the evolution of the galaxies as well as of this or that tribe or society. Rarely in fact has a theory connected with a particular science had such wide acceptance, perhaps because the theory of evolution itself, instead of being a scientific theory that became popularized, began as a general tendency that entered into the domain of biology. For this very reason it soon gained acceptance more as a dogma than as a useful scientific hypothesis.

From the metaphysical point of view the reality of a species is not exhausted by its purely material manifestations. Like other things the species is an 'idea' whose imprint in material form does not confine and exhaust its essential reality which remains independent of matter. A species could not evolve into another because each species is an independent reality qualitatively different from another. As is true of the domain of quality in general each quality is an independent reality even if materially produced by others as exemplified in the case of colours where a colour produced by the mixture of two other colours is itself a new and independent quality. As far as the species are concerned they are, from the metaphysical point of view, ultimately so many 'ideas' in the Divine Mind which at a particular cosmic moment have become imprinted in the corporeal world and retain their reality on other planes of existence—whatever their careers and histories in the corporeal domain. Most of all, metaphysics and also logic cannot accept the possibility of the greater coming into being from the lesser, unless it is already there one way or another. Consciousness or the spirit could not evolve from matter unless it were already present anteriorly to matter, just as one could not physically lift an object against a gravitational field, unless there were already a reserve of energy in the mover.

Moreover, from the metaphysical point of view the effect can never be divorced from its cause. The world can never be totally separated from its Creator, and there is no logical or philosophical reason whatsoever to refuse the possibility of continuous creation or a series of creations as all traditional doctrines have held. The understanding of metaphysics could at least make clear the often forgotten fact that the plausibility of the theory of evolution is based on several non-scientific factors belonging to the general philosophical climate of eighteenth-century and nineteenth-century Europe such as belief in progress, Deism which cut off the hands of the Creator from His creation and the reduction of reality to the two levels of mind and matter. Only with such beliefs could the theory of evolution appear as 'rational', and the most easy to accept for a world which had completely lost sight of the multiple levels of being and had reduced nature to a purely corporeal world totally cut off from any other order of existence.

In the light of this background, biologists and geologists have come to uphold the theory of evolution,[19] and usually refuse even to submit it to a methodological and scientific scrutiny or allow it to be questioned like any other scientific hypothesis.[20] In most books written on the subject facts are marshalled in such a way as to present evolution as an established fact. Rarely have the views of respected scientists who have opposed evolution been presented, because evolution has come to gain a status in biological and geological circles very different from what one finds in any other science.

But opposition to the theory of evolution continues on scientific lines and in fact has increased in the past few years. It was not only the nineteenth century naturalists and biologists like Louis Agassiz who opposed Darwinian evolution, but also some contemporary scientists like Bounoure, Bertrand-Sernet, Collins, Clark, Caullery, Lemoine, Dewar, Grant-Watson and many others.[21] The arguments presented by such men are all of a scientific nature rather than being theological or metaphysical. There is first of all the assertion made by Lemoine and others that the palaeontological evidence upon which evolutionists base their arguments in fact contradicts evolution[22] and that the argument is circular.[23] The geologic record shows sudden explosions of new species which some evolutionists have sought to explain through the theory of 'quanta of evolution' (*tachygenesis*), or the 'systematic suppression of origins' proposed by Teilhard de Chardin. But neither of these theories stands scientific criticism, and the difficulty remains that contrary to evolutionary theory each new species makes its entrance upon the stage of life very suddenly and over an extended region.[24] Nor does the established fact that in the geologic record there is a gradation of fauna prove evolution of one form into another, since each fauna arises suddenly with all its essential characteristics.[25]

The great types of zoology have been shown by some scientists to be independent of each other and without a specific position on the palaeontological record.[26] The few cases where the actual process of transformation has been described by biologists have shown themselves to be combined with obstacles which make them appear as miraculous, to say the least.[27] The family trees of biology first drawn by Haeckel, and now popular mainstays of books on biology, are shown to contain overt contradictions and to be based more on fantasy than on scientific evidence. These and many other arguments are presented by a minority of biologists and geologists whose voice the present mental climate does not allow to be fully heard.

In the whole question of evolutionary theory and its implications a clear distinction is not made between objective and subjective elements. Taken as a dogma, evolution is presented without considering biological cases which cannot be explained by it.[28] Likewise, the opposition of the evolutionary hypothesis to the law of entropy, and the implications it has in the light of the belief held by other sciences of the gradual running down of the whole corporeal universe, is rarely emphasized in general presentations of evolution which is made to appear as most logical and scientific. Most important of all, few bother to mention that in the world in which we live there is no evolution observed at all.[29] Nor have the experiments made to provide a laboratory case of the transformation of one species into another been successful.[30]

What is more, there are species that have survived from the first geologic age without evolving at all. If we were to make a truly scientific statement about the world of life about us we would have to say in fact that nature presents to us species that are constant and unchanging but who occasionally die and disappear.[31]

If we have repeated these scientific criticisms of evolution here, it is not to open a biological debate but to distinguish between scientific facts and the philosophical assumptions that underlie them. A re-discovery of metaphysics would be particularly pertinent in this case because it would remove this philosophical obstacle and allow biological and geological facts to be discussed and debated, as in other sciences, without reliance upon evolution as a dogma which cannot be challenged. Furthermore, it would prevent the abuse of evolutionary theory in other fields, a practice which is very widespread to the extent that even contradictory philosophical views appeal to evolution as their 'scientific' justification.[32] This is particularly important as far as man's encounter with nature is concerned because pseudo-philosophies of this kind can do the greatest damage to the harmony between man and nature, by presenting man as the inevitable victor of a long struggle who therefore has the right to conquer and dominate all things or by destroying the spiritual significance of nature which depends precisely on the fact that it reflects an abiding and permanent reality beyond itself.

Pseudo-philosophies become even more dangerous when they begin to incorporate religious elements and present themselves as a synthesis of science and religion, or of religion based on scientific facts, which in reality are no more than hypotheses supported by a particular philosophical attitude. The case of Teilhard de Chardin, the most recent adventure of this kind, is a perfect example of pseudo-metaphysics tied to the theory of evolution, and stands at the very antipodes and is the antithesis of the spiritual vision of nature we have discussed in our earlier chapters.

What is desperately needed in biology, as in physics, is a philosophy of nature which again cannot be abstracted from biology itself and even less from physics. The debate between teleology and mechanism reflects so clearly an inert view of nature drawn from physics forced upon the sciences of life. For this reason many outstanding biologists have rebelled against the mechanistic thesis and asserted the importance of teleology in all life processes.[33] In other questions of biology difficulties are also encountered because the philosophical assumptions are those of a world seen through the eyes of physics. There has been as yet no philosophy of biology which does justice to the subject of this science even less than that found in the case of physics.[34] And in biology, even more than in the sciences dealing with quantity, there is a need for a vision of reality in which qualities and forms of life have an ontological rather than an accidental status. Such vision can only find its justification within that ultimate science of reality that is metaphysics.

Metaphysical doctrines can also assist in the elimination of false implications in biological theories, especially those of the theory of evolution. Throughout the world today particularly in the Orient where there are still societies that remain faithful to their religious principles and the social structure based upon them, men are asked to evolve and change simply because evolution is in the nature of things and is inevitable. A more objective assessment of the findings of biology would insist that as long as man has been living on earth he has not evolved at all; nor has his natural environment changed in any way. The same plants and animals are still born, grow, wither and die and regenerate themselves except for the unfortunate species that modern man who believes himself to belong to the process of evolution has made extinct. In fact it could be asserted that although the rise, change, and decay of human societies is an inevitable truth the one factor that has not evolved throughout this process is nature itself. The so-called progressive evolution of mankind, far from being the inevitable consequence of cosmic and natural processes, is completely opposed to the immediate and contemporary life of the natural environment in which man lives, an environment whose movement is cyclic rather than evolutionary and which through cyclic change reproduces the same permanent forms.[35] Perhaps one of the reasons why modern man who believes in progress and evolution has come to a severe crisis in his encounter with nature is that his evolutionary beliefs with all that these beliefs imply religiously, politically, socially and economically do not conform to the life in that domain of reality that surrounds him but which he has not made, namely virgin nature and all the forms of life flourishing in its bosom.

The application of metaphysical principles to other sciences such as chemistry, geology, astronomy or mathematics itself[36] could be continued along the lines mentioned briefly as providing both an overall matrix and a criterion for judging between hypotheses and facts and between scientific discoveries and their so-called philosophical implications. The examples cited concerning physics and biology suffice, however, in this brief exposition to indicate the principle we have in mind. In each case metaphysical knowledge does not grow out of an experimental science but stands as a universal science which provides the general background for each science and which brings to light the universal and symbolic significance of the discoveries of each science, a process which the sciences cannot carry out themselves by virtue of the self-imposed restriction of dealing only with facts and generalizations or mental constructions based upon them and not with the symbolic significance of facts or phenomena.

In this domain metaphysics can also render another service of great value, namely bringing to light the true significance of the traditional sciences of nature which, because of the loss of metaphysical knowledge, have lost their meaning. Only a re-discovery of the doctrine of the multiple states of being, of cosmic correspondences and of the science of symbolism can reveal again the meaning of such sciences as alchemy or astrology. There is no validity in the assertion that modern man can no longer see God in the sun and the sky except if one means by this that man has closed his eyes to this aspect of things. Otherwise the structure of reality has not changed. Only man's vision of it has altered.

but the appearance has . . .

No matter how deeply one pierces into the depths of cosmic space or the heart of the atom, the structure of reality taught by metaphysical doctrines, and the traditional cosmological sciences that are their extension, remain unchanged and unaffected. All extensions of modern scientific knowledge are horizontal in the domain of corporeal and material existence, even if it be galactic matter, and thus do not in the least affect other planes of existence. Moreover, this extended knowledge of material things is itself in need of the synthetic cosmological knowledge provided by the traditional sciences of the cosmos. Man's intelligence is made so that he can come to know with certainty the Infinite and the Absolute, not the indefinite and the relative. Knowledge that is concerned solely with the material world is dealing truly with the indefinite, or at least its quantitative aspect, with what the Hindus call the cosmic labyrinth or *māya* and the Buddhists *samsāra*. Although legitimate as all other knowledge, this form of science can remain wholesome only when cultivated in the matrix of a science that is centred on the Absolute and the Infinite and can thus, by virtue of this immutable centre, locate and define the periphery and the relative with which the modern sciences are concerned. In this task revitalized cosmological sciences, again made meaningful through metaphysical knowledge, could play a vital role as the link between the modern sciences and purely metaphysical doctrines themselves, as a bridge between the modern scientific knowledge of nature and gnosis that deals with realities beyond all cosmic manifestation.

Such a revitalization of the traditional sciences, however, requires a re-discovery of the true meaning of symbolism and the education of modern man to understand the language of symbolism in the same way that he is taught to master the languages of logic or mathematics. This century has been witness to the re-discovery of the significance of myth and symbol,[37] but this event has as yet had little effect upon theology, science or even art. Modern man too rarely understands the meaning of symbols and due to his lack of discriminative knowledge is apt to mistake forms and signs of diabolical origin with symbols whose source is transcendental and luminous. Much of the poetry and painting that is so-called symbolic and the Jungian search for the origin of symbols in a collective unconscious that is like the rubbish-heap of a particular culture or ethnic group bear witness to this fact. Symbolism, in the essential meaning of the term we have in mind, is concerned with the process of sacralization of the cosmos. It is through the symbol that man is able to find meaning in the cosmic environment that surrounds him.[38] It is the symbol that reveals objective reality as sacred; in fact all that is objective reality is sacred and symbolic of a reality that lies beyond it.[39] Only the Origin or the One is completely real and totally Itself and not the symbol of something other than Itself. Everything else is a symbol of a state of being that transcends it. It can be said that even the void and nihilism felt by modern man is a symbol, a symbol of the transcendent aspect of God who, after bestowing all qualities, also takes all qualities back unto Himself. The profane itself symbolizes a religious reality in the same way that 'Satan is the ape of God'. Yet one must already be possessed of the knowledge of symbolism and the principles it involves in order to discern in every situation the symbolic meaning inherent in it.

In fact to understand fully the meaning of symbolism, of the symbolic meaning of forms, colours and shapes, of all that surrounds us, is a way to see God everywhere. It is thus a way of making all things sacred. For this very reason it requires metaphysical discrimination and a conformity to Pure Being which is the source of all symbols.[40] It needs an education in the deepest meaning of the word, a re-orientation of man so that he becomes aware of the transparent nature of the world that surrounds him and the transcendent dimension that is present in every cosmic situation.

To instruct men to understand symbols in this manner does not mean a negation of the factual aspect of things. Rather, it means a revelation of the knowledge of another aspect of things which is even more real and more closely tied to their existential root than the sensible qualities and the quantitative aspect with which modern science is concerned. To teach the significance of the tree as the symbol of the multiple states of being, or of the mountain as the symbol of the cosmos, or the sun as the symbol of the intelligible principle of the Universe does not in any way detract from the discoveries of botany, geology or astronomy. But if nature is to be possessed of meaning again, and if the encounter of man and nature is to avoid the disasters and calamities that threaten it today, this symbolic knowledge must be presented, not as poetic fantasy but as a science tied to the ontological root of things. The symbolic nature of the tree or the mountain is as closely a part of its being as the bark of the tree or the granite rocks of the mountain. A true symbol is no more man-made than the properties of the bark or the granite. It is only in this light, as a science of natural forms that complements modern scientific knowledge, that the science of symbols can play a vital role in restoring man to his home in the Universe. Moreover, this science can also aid in increasing the understanding of those particular symbols which Christianity like every other religion has sanctified, symbols the forgetting of which has forced many an intelligent soul to search for answers to pressing questions outside the teachings of the Church.

Yet another application of metaphysical principles concerns not so much the domain of knowledge but that of action. It concerns the application of modern science whether it be in technology or in war. In fact the anxiety of most of those who have at last become interested in the question of the relation of man and nature springs up usually not from theoretical considerations but from observing the unbelievable horrors of war which the applications of modern science have made possible. In this domain unending debates continue and as so often happens these days a situation is created where no clear cut answer is found, precisely because the ground has not been prepared properly.

Some believe there are things worth fighting for and even dying for and others for whom the terrestrial life of man is the ultimate end therefore do not believe it is worth jeopardizing this existence for any reason whatsoever even if the price be the loss of the dignity which makes man human rather than animal. Further, when the immediate question of this alternative concerning war is not being considered the focus of attention is usually turned to the peaceful extension of technology which is supposed to obliterate all misery on earth but which usually brings with it greater problems than those it succeeds in solving. In all these questions of a political, social and economic nature metaphysical principles can also cast some light not by providing a painless solution to a particular predicament where one must accept the reaction of an action committed but by revealing the principial causes that have brought about a particular situation. They can most of all dispel the illusion about the existence of that purely economic being whose indefinite material progress is supposed to be the goal of every social and political organization. They can help to correct some of the errors of other sciences concerned with man and society which still copy blindly the methods of seventeenth-century physics and study man without knowing what he really is. They can also set bounds upon the application of technology and in fact upon this unrelenting drive to satisfy man's animal desires and even to create new needs and desires when possible.

In the same way that the rise of a purely material and quantitative science of nature in the West is due to deep rooted causes and certain limitations in the theological formulations of Latin Christianity, which at the moment of the weakening of faith led to the divorce between science and religion, so does the illimitable and unrestricted application of modern science in the West in the form of technology depend on the fact that Christianity is a religion without a Sacred Law or as Muslims would say without a *Sharī'ah*.[41]

This fact may not be evident for a Christian who sees his religion as the norm with which he compares other religions, but it becomes obvious if a comparison is made with the other monotheistic religions issuing from the 'Abrahamic tree', namely Judaism and Islam. Both of these religions have a Sacred Law, the

Talmudic and the Quranic, which are inseparable from the revelation of each religion. In fact in both cases the will of God is seen as manifested in concrete laws which theoretically govern all aspects of human life and are the blueprint of the perfect human society. Man's political, social and economic life is governed by the divine injunctions contained in the Sacred Law.

Christianity, on the other hand in conformity with its esoteric character, came as a spiritual way without a Sacred Law. Christ brought a way that was not of this world and a set of exalted spiritual teachings which can be followed fully only by a society of saints. As it became the religion of a civilization it incorporated Roman and even common law into its structure and while the unity of medieval Christendom lasted the law was given a divine sanction as we see in the theological discussions of St Thomas on natural and divine law. But the fact remained that the laws that governed the political, social and economic life of men did not enjoy the same direct authority of revelation as the teachings of Christ which concern general spiritual principles such as the necessity to be charitable. Men continued to accept the virtue of charity, but once the unity of Christendom was destroyed they began to interpret in different ways exactly what was meant by being charitable. It is a paradox of modern Western history that every politico-economic system, even those that are most secular and anti-Christian, makes of charity the supreme virtue, even if it is only charity towards man considered as an animal. Even in Marxism the supreme virtue is charity which in this case has become a parody of the charity of the saints.

The lack of a Sacred Law in Christianity not only made social upheavals easier but also facilitated the disruption of nature through its unrestricted and unlimited exploitation. The development of economics as an independent discipline, whose subject is man considered solely as a being with material needs, is a result of a situation in which there is no direct religious instruction as to what man's rights and obligations are toward both nature and God. It is of course true that Christian theology has influenced social and economic attitudes throughout the ages. The

134

no such person exists...

debate about faith and good works, or the glorification of work among New England Puritans is only too well known. But theological views are not the same as revealed law. The very fact that there was not within Christianity a detailed instruction about social structure and economic practices led, with a weakening of Christianity in the West, through economic practices and applications of technology to an amassment of wealth which knows no bounds and limits. It has also led to the creation of a modern civilization which has spread to other continents and has brought about political and military situations in which the choice has often had to be made between annihilation and the sacrifice of those values which give dignity to human life.

A re-discovery of metaphysical knowledge, and a revitalization of a theology and philosophy of nature could set a limit upon the application of science and technology. In the old days man had to be saved from nature. Today nature has to be saved from man in both peace and war.[42] Many labour under the illusion that only war is evil and that if only it could be averted man could go on peacefully to create paradise on earth. What is forgotten is that in both the state of war and peace man is waging an incessant war upon nature. The official state of war is no more than an occasional outburst of an activity that goes on all the time within the souls of men, in human society and towards nature. It is no more than a chimerical dream to expect to have peace based upon a state of intense war toward nature and disequilibrium with the cosmic environment. It is only the complete ignorance of what man's relation to nature means that could allow such views to be entertained. Whether one pollutes water resources in a single bombing or does so over a twenty-year period is essentially the same; the only difference is the matter of time. The net result does not differ in the two cases because in both instances man is waging war against nature.

Perhaps the answer to the burning question of how to avoid war and also of how to preserve human dignity in face of the threat of total war, lies in coming to peace with nature. But the development of this peaceful accord depends in turn upon the re-discovery of the spiritual significance of nature. With the help of metaphysical principles and a re-awakening of interest in the tradition within Christianity that has had a spiritual vision of nature a love of nature based on the science of its symbolic and ontological reality can be developed and indeed must be developed.[43] In this way, a harmonious relation can be created for all those who are able to understand and grasp this metaphysical knowledge which leads to a love and respect for nature.

Of course the feasibility of applying the programme proposed in these chapters, and the question of whether the proposals of this kind ever have the chance of being carried out in a world which does not seem to want to change its course until events force it to do so is itself a matter to consider, one which however important we cannot treat here. Our task, rather, has been to make this analysis concerning the causes of the crisis in the encounter of man and nature and to propose means whereby this crisis can be ameliorated. Whether any suggestions of a spiritual and intellectual nature will be heard by a world which has turned its ears to the sound and fury of its own making and become deaf to all other voices remains to be seen. The attempt to think of this major problem and to provide an answer is nevertheless itself worth while, for to seek to discover the truth in any matter is the most constructive of all acts.

In the end what we can say with all certainty is that there is no peace possible among men unless there is peace and harmony with nature. And in order to have peace and harmony with nature one must be in harmony and equilibrium with Heaven, and ultimately with the Source and Origin of all things.[44] He who is at peace with God is also at peace with His creation, both with nature and with man.

NOTES TO CHAPTER IV

1. '*Il y a des critiques littéraires et des critiques d'art. Pourquoi n'y aurait-il pas de critiques scientifiques?*' M. Ollivier, *Physique moderne et réalité*, Paris, 1962, p. 58.

2. *Ibid.*, p. 9.

3. As far as the true meaning of the occult sciences and spiritism are concerned see R. Guénon, *L'Erreur spirite*, Paris, 1923; also his *Symboles fondamentaux de la science sacrée*, Paris, 1962.

4. 'Wild Nature is at one with holy poverty and also with spiritual childlikeness; she is an open book containing an inexhaustible teaching of truth and beauty. It is in the midst of his own artifices that man most easily becomes corrupted, it is they that make him covetous and impious; close to virgin Nature, who knows neither agitation nor falsehood, he had the hope of remaining contemplative like Nature herself. And it is Nature, quasi-divine in her totality, who will have the final word.' Schuon, *Light on the Ancient Worlds*, p. 84.

5. 'Nature inviolate is at once a vestige of the Earthly Paradise and a prefiguration of the Heavenly Paradise. . . .' Schuon, *op. cit.*, p. 143.

6. 'Christianity, having had to react against a wholly "pagan" spirit (in the Biblical sense) has at the same time caused to disappear—as always happens in such cases—values which did not deserve the reproach of paganism. Having to oppose, among the Mediterraneans, a philosophic and "flat" naturalism, it suppressed at the same time, amongst the Nordics, a "naturism" of spiritual character. Modern technology is the result—very indirect no doubt—of a perspective which, having banished from nature the gods and the genies, and, having also, by this very fact, rendered it profane, has ended by allowing it to be "profaned" in the most brutal sense of the word. The Promethean Westerner—but not every Westerner—is affected by a kind of innate contempt for nature; for him nature is a property to be enjoyed or exploited, or even an enemy to conquer.' F. Schuon, 'The Symbolist Outlook', *Tomorrow*, Winter, 1966, pp. 54–5.

7. See W. J. Ong, 'Religion, Scholarship and the Restitution of Man', *Daedalus*, XCI Spring, 1962, where he speaks of the need to reunite 'the interior and exterior, to restore man to his home in the cosmos'. pp. 428–9.

8. 'In a sense, metaphysics and science are complementary. Metaphysics does not deal with the detailed behaviour of nature, science does not deal with the ultimate interpretation of natural knowledge. They are both necessary to a synthetic view of the world. But the relation is one-sided; science cannot begin without assuming a metaphysical principle, whereas metaphysics does not presuppose any scientific principle for the validity of its conclusions. One of the functions of metaphysics is to examine the grounds for the presuppositions of science, just as one function of logic is to lay bare these presuppositions. But this does not exhaust metaphysics. . . .' Caldin, *The Power and Limits of Science, A Philosophical Study*, p. 117.

9. 'Physics is restricted by its own method, and cannot be expected to yield a full account of experience: it cannot deal with the fundamentals of rational thought and action, it omits considerations of qualities, of forms, of agents and causality. Accordingly the knowledge of nature provided by its theoretical interpretations is very limited; but these limitations do not carry consequences outside physics. A philosophy cannot, then, be based on physics alone; not only would it have to leave unexplained the basic assumptions of physics, but it would be absurdly limited in scope.' Caldin, *op. cit.*, pp. 47–8.

'What must be immediately apparent is that physical science has abstracted certain measurable quantities from an altogether richer reality, and has concerned itself with these, and these alone, to the exclusion of everything else which is of interest.' Yarnold, *The Spiritual Crisis of the Scientific Age*, p. 28.

See also Mascall, *Christian Theology and Natural Science*, chap. II; and Smethurst, *Modern Science and Christian Belief*, chap. V.

10. Eddington cites the story of the ichthyologist who uses a particular size net to catch fish from the sea and then arrives at the conclusion that all fish in the sea are of that particular size. See Eddington, *The Philosophy of Physical Science*, p. 16.

11. 'The fact that experiment is made imposes a strict limitation on the general conclusions. They are valid within the context of the experiment and the experimenter.' Yarnold, *op. cit.*, pp. 16–17

12. 'But we have seen that science concerns itself with only a part of what we can perceive, and so the knowledge of the natural world that could be gained by the use of all our faculties that can bring us in relation with it greatly exceeds and transcends that which can be acquired by the use of the scientific method. We must set up the ideal of a *sapientia naturalis*, a wisdom concerning nature to which our present *scientia* or knowledge is a valid contribution.' Sherwood Taylor, *The Fourfold Vision*, p. 84.

13. 'Physical science then, is not an adequate description of nature; it is a portrait made by an observer with a particular point of view and a definite limitation on his vision. He selects the data, somewhat as an artist selects. Science is a construction, made by synthesizing selected data; it is not an untouched vision of nature. Certainly it gives us some understanding of the order of nature's workings, but not a full understanding. Moreover, it entirely neglects the relation of nature to man and to the first cause. From natural science we cannot learn what material nature is for, how and why it exists at all, and why it has any laws. The beauty of nature, then, in its widest sense, is not to be apprehended through science alone . . . Besides the minute investigations of science and the unification of them that theoretical

science effects, we need to understand the relation of nature to man and God . . .
We need a wisdom that transcends science if we are to have a full view of
nature. Science alone will not give us the conceptions we need for a full
knowledge of nature . . .' Caldin, *op. cit.*, pp. 130–1.

14. 'The least phenomenon participates in several continuities or cosmic
dimensions, incommensurable in relation to each other . . .' Burckhardt,
'Cosmology and Modern Science', *Tomorrow*, Autumn, 1964, p. 308.

15. See Lord Northbourne, 'Pictures of the Universe'; *Tomorrow*, Autumn,
1964, pp. 267–78.

16. On this and other contradictions in modern physical theories see M.
Ollivier, *Physique moderne et réalité.*

17. On the 'perfect' science and its comparison with modern science see
F. Brunner, *Science et réalité*, Paris, 1954, where he writes, '*La science
parfaite, si elle existe, n'est pas, comme la science moderne, une démarche de la
raison individuelle, liée aux données limitées de l'expérimentation et du calcul.
Relative à l'origine, à l'être et à la fin absolue des choses, sa propriété est
d'être tout entière suspendue à la connaissance du Principe de l'univers.*' (pp.
8–9).

18. '. . . for Jung, the "collective unconscious" is stiuated "below", at the
level of physiological instinct: it is important to bear this in mind since the
term "collective unconscious", in itself, could carry a wider and in some
sort more spiritual meaning, as certain assimilations made by Jung seem to
suggest, especially his utilizing – or rather in point of fact his usurping – the
term "archetype". . .' Burckhardt, 'Cosmology and Modern Science',
Tomorrow, Winter, 1965, p. 27. 'Jung breached certain strictly materialistic
frameworks of modern science; but this fact is of no use to anyone, to say
the least—one would have liked to rejoice over it—because the influences
that infiltrate through this breach come from the inferior psychism and not
from the Spirit, which alone is true and alone able to save us.' *Ibid.*, p. 55.

19. One of the great French biologists writes, '*Bref, on nous demande ici
un acte de foi, et c'est bien en effet sous la forme d'une vérité révélée que chacun
de nous a reçu jadis la notion d'évolution.*' L. Bounoure, *Déterminisme et
finalité double loi de la vie*, Paris, 1957. See also the same author's *Recherche
d'une doctrine de la vie*, Paris, 1964, for a biological criticism of evolution and
some of its defenders.

20. 'The concept of organic Evolution is very highly prized by biologists,
for many of whom it is an object of genuinely religious devotion, because
they regard it as a supreme integrative principle. This is probably the reason
why the severe methodological criticism employed in other departments of
biology has not yet been brought to bear against evolutionary speculation.'
Thompson, *Science and Common Sense*, p. 229.

We recall once in a class of stratigraphy when we asked the professor a question which seemed to criticize the postulate of evolution he answered curtly, 'We no longer ask questions about evolution. We only accept and follow it.'

21. Only too often the works of such authors have been deliberately neglected or suppressed. A case in point is the work by D. Dewar called the *Transformist Illusion,* Murfreesboro, 1957, which has assembled a vast amount of palaeontological and biological evidence against evolution. The author who was an evolutionist in his youth wrote many monographs which exist in the libraries of comparative zoology and biology everywhere. But his last work, *The Transformist Illusion,* had to be published in Murfreesboro, Tennessee(!) and is not easy to find even in libraries that have all his earlier works. There is hardly any other field of science where such obscurantist practices are prevalent.

22. Lemoine, a French geologist, as the editor of a volume of the French encyclopaedia on Living Organisms after reviewing articles by different contributors on the palaeontological proofs of evolution writes; 'It follows from this account that the theory of evolution is impossible. In reality, despite appearances, no one any longer believes in it, and one speaks, without attaching any importance to it, of evolution to denote linkage—or more evolved, less evolved in the sense of more perfected, less perfected, because it is the conventional language, admitted and almost obligatory in the scientific world. Evolution is a kind of dogma, in which the priests no longer believe, but which they maintain for their people.' Quoted by Dewar in *Transformist Illusion,* p. 262.

23. '*De là vient que l'évolutionisme repose tout entier sur une vaste pétition de principe: les faits paléontologiques sont utilisés pour prouver l'évolution et, à la fois, trouvent leur explication dans cette théorie inventée pour eux. C'est un magnifique exemple de* circulus vitiosus. Bounoure, *Déterminisme et finalité,* pp. 80–1.

24. For a criticism of these theories which seek to provide an answer for the explosion of new forms see Bounoure, *op. cit.,* pp. 65 ff.

25. '*Qu'il y ait eu, au cours des âges, une certaine gradation des formes, cela est certain, mais ne prouve nullement un rapport de descendence entre les différents groupes, dont chacun, au contraire, surgit brusquement,* de novo, *avec tous ses caractères essentiels.*' Bounoure, *op. cit.,* pp. 57–8.

26. '*La majeure partie des types foundamentaux du regne animal se presentent à nous sans aucun lieu an point de vue paléontologique.*' C. Depéret, *Les Transformations du monde animal,* Paris, 1907, p. 76.

27. See Dewar, *The Transformist Illusion,* Chapter XVII, 'Some Transformations Postulated by the Doctrine of Evolution.'

28. See the various studies of E. L. Grant-Watson such as *Nature Abounding*, London, 1941; *Enigmas of Natural History*, London (n.d.), and *The Mystery of Physical Life*, London, 1964, where such cases are studied. The author seeks in these works to study the 'wisdom of nature' by turning to specific cases where this 'wisdom' is most directly manifested.

29. '*Quoi qu'il en soit, dans le monde actuel, nous ne constatons aucun signe d'évolution; celle-ci parait exclue du monde vivant que nous avons sous les yeux et dont nous faisons partie.*' Bounoure, *Déterminisme et finalité*, p. 51.

30. M. Caullery, *Le Problème de l'évolution*, Paris, 1931, p. 401; Bounoure, *op. cit.*, pp. 50–1.

31. '*Elles* [*espèces*] *n'ont devant elles qu'une alternative: ou se maintenir inchangés, on s'éteindre.*' Caullery, *op. cit.*, pp. 84–5.

32. '*Le succès de la théorie évolutioniste, c'est le succès des personnes faciles, il n'est point de bio-philosophie qui ne recoure à cette fille complaisante: elle sert le matérialisme de Haeckel et de Lyssenko, le panthéisme de Teilhard de Chardin, le lyrisme éperdu de Saint-Seine, l'anti-hasard de Cuénot, le spiritualisme de Le Roy et de Leconte de Noüy, l'orthodoxie religieuse des prêtres, moines et princes de grand' clergie. Il existe aujourd'hui un scientisme clérical dont l'ardent empressement est manifeste pour l'évolution: chez celle-ci se reconcilient les passionés de l'athéisme et les croyants de stricte obédience.*' Bounoure, *op. cit.*, p. 78.

33. Such an outstanding biologist as D'Arcy Thomson is an example.

34. On the problems concerned with the philosophy of biology see E. W. F. Tomlin, *Living and Knowing*, London, 1955, parts two and three.

35. This assertion is not meant in any way to be opposed to the gradual solidification and coagulation of the cosmic ambiance asserted by traditional doctrines, especially the Hindu doctrines of cosmic cycles.

36. As far as mathematics is concerned an example of how metaphysical principles can be applied and the metaphysical significance of a branch of mathematics elucidated can be found in R. Guénon, *Les Principes du calcul infinitésmial*, Paris, 1946.

37. The writings of traditional authors like R. Guénon, A. K. Coomaraswamy, F. Schuon and T. Burckhardt as well as such well-known academic figures as H. Zimmer and M. Eliade are especially significant in this domain.

38. 'The religious symbol translates a human situation into cosmological terms and vice versa; more precisely, it reveals the continuity between the structures of human existence and cosmic structures. This means that man does not feel himself "isolated" in the cosmos, but that he "opens out" to a world which, thanks to a symbol, proves "familiar". On the other hand, the cosmological values of symbols enable him to leave behind the subjectivity

of a situation and to recognize the objectivity of his personal experiences.'
M. Eliade, 'Methodological Remarks on the Study of Religious Symbolism',
in M. Eliade and J. Kitagawa (ed.), *The History of Religions – Essays in
Methodology*, Chicago, 1959, p. 103.

39. 'Religious symbols are capable of revealing a modality of the real or a
structure of the World that is not evident on the level of immediate experience. . . .'

'For the primitive, *symbols are always religious* because they point to something *real* or to a *structure of the world*. For on the archaic levels of culture,
the *real*—that is, the powerful, the meaningful, the living—is equivalent to
the sacred.' Eliade, *op. cit.*, pp. 98–9.

40. 'The science of symbols—not simply a knowledge of traditional symbols—
proceeds from the qualitative significances of substances, forms, spatial
directions . . . and other properties or state of things; we are not dealing here
with subjective appreciations, for the cosmic qualities are ordered both in
relation to Being and according to a hierarchy which is more real than the
individual; they are, then, independent of our tastes, or rather they determine them to the extent that we are ourselves conformable to Being; we
assent to the qualities to the extent that we ourselves are "qualitative".
Symbolism, whether it resides in nature or whether it is affirmed in sacred
art, also corresponds to a manner of "seeing God everywhere", on condition that this vision is spontaneous thanks to an intimate knowledge of
the principles from which the science of symbols proceeds. . . .' F. Schuon,
Gnosis Divine Wisdom (trans. G. E. H. Palmer), London, 1959, p. 110.

41. On the special character of Christianity as a spiritual way without a law
in comparison to Judaism and Islam see F. Schuon, *The Transcendent Unity
of Religions* (trans. P. Townsend), London, 1948, Chaps. VI and VII.

42. 'Because of the true man's totality and centrality he has the almost
divine function of guardianship over the world of nature. Once this role is
ignored or misused he is in danger of being shown ultimately by nature who
in reality is the conqueror and who the conquered. It could also be said that
in the past man had to protect himself from the forces of nature, whereas
today it is nature which must be protected from man.' J. E. Brown, 'The
Spiritual Legacy of the American Indian', *Tomorrow*, Autumn, 1964, p. 302.

43. 'This dethronement of nature, or this scission between men and the
earth—a reflection of the scission between man and Heaven—has borne such
bitter fruits that it should not be difficult to show how, in these days, the
timeless message of nature constitutes a viaticum of the first importance.
Some may object that the West has always known—especially in the eighteenth
and nineteenth centuries—returns to virgin nature, but this is besides the
point, as it is not here a question of a "naturism" that might well be de-

ṣcribed as romantic and "deist" or even atheist. It is not a question of projecting a supersaturated and disillusioned individualism into a desacrated nature—this would be a piece of wordliness like any other—but, on the contrary, of finding again in nature, on the basis of a traditional outlook, the divine substance which is inherent in it; in other words, to "see God everywhere", and to see nothing apart from His mysterious presence.' F. Schuon, 'The Symbolist Outlook', pp. 55–6.

44. 'The clear understanding of the virtue of Heaven and Earth is what is called "The Great Root", and "The Great Origin";—they who have it are in harmony with Heaven, and so they produce all equable arrangement in the world;—they are those who are in harmony with men.' *The Sacred Books of China, The Texts of Taoism* (trans. J. Legge), vol. I, p. 332.

INDEX

145

Man and Nature